# ON HUMAN FINERY

*PLATE I*

Dessiné par Doerow                    Gravé par Figuard

Conspicuous Leisure

# ON HUMAN FINERY

*By*

QUENTIN BELL

THE HOGARTH PRESS
40-42 WILLIAM IV STREET
LONDON, W.C.2
1948

PUBLISHED BY
The Hogarth Press Ltd
LONDON

✷

Oxford University Press
TORONTO

*First impression,* 1947
*Second impression,* 1948

# CONTENTS

# ILLUSTRATIONS

## Colour Plates

## Monochrome Plates

TO

MLLE. JANE SIMONE BUSSY

# FOREWORD

THIS is not a work of erudition but of theory; the reader who seeks erudition will find an abundance in other works of which those mentioned below form but a small sample. Works of a purely theoretical nature are less common, but many scholars have given us their conclusions together with their observations.

It will be found that I have made a decided attack upon the theoretical constructions of several writers, and, among others, those scholars to whom I am most profoundly indebted. I must confess, though it can but aggravate the charge of ingratitude, that in many cases my debt has been not only of that kind which arises from the necessities of ignorance, but also of a direct nature: an author may stimulate or instruct even when he fails to convince.

The following works have been consulted:

Max von Boehn, *Modes and Manners* (*Die Mode*). Eng. tr. by Joan Joshua. London, 1932.
Flugel, Professor J. C., *The Psychology of Clothes*. London, 1930.
Laver, *Taste and Fashion*. London, 1937.
London Museum Catalogue, No. 5 (Costume).
Nystrom, Paul H., *The Economics of Fashion*. New York, 1928.
Poiret, Paul, *En habillant l'époque*. Paris, 1930.
Price, J., *Dame Fashion*. London, 1913.
Schwabe and Kelly, *A Short History of Costume in England*.
Webb, W. M., *The Heritage of Dress*. London, 1907.
C. Willet Cunnington, *English Women's Clothing in the 19th Century*. London, 1937.

Where other sources have been used they are acknowledged in footnotes.

Grateful mention should also be made of Mr. C.

Willet Cunnington's theoretical work, *Why Women Wear Clothes*, of Mr. Gerald Heard's *Narcissus, an Anatomy of Clothes*, and above all of Thorstein Veblen's *The Theory of the Leisure Class*, all quotations from which are taken from the 1934 edition in the Modern Library series published in New York.

I have the greatest pleasure in acknowledging the assistance that I have received in obtaining illustrations from the British Museum, the National Gallery, the National Portrait Gallery, *The Times*, the proprietors of *Punch* and of *Vogue*, the Ronald Press Co. of New York, Flammarion of Paris, and am particularly beholden to Messrs. Harrods who have been most kind, also to my sister Mrs. David Garnett who has allowed me to make use of her large collection of fashion plates.

# CHAPTER ONE

# SARTORIAL MORALITY

No one finds difficulty in assenting to the commonplace that the greater part of the expenditure incurred by all classes for apparel is incurred for the sake of respectable appearance rather than for the protection of the person. And probably at no other point is the sense of shabbiness so keenly felt as it is if we fall short of the standard set by social usage in this matter of dress. It is true of dress in even a higher degree than of most other items of consumption, that people will undergo a very considerable degree of privation in the comforts or necessaries of life in order to afford what is considered a decent amount of wasteful consumption; so that it is by no means an uncommon occurrence, in an inclement climate, for people to go ill clad in order to appear well dressed. And the commercial value of the goods used for clothing in any modern community is made up to a much larger extent of the fashionableness, the reputability of the goods than of the mechanical service which they render in clothing the person of the wearer. The need of dress is eminently a "higher" or spiritual need.

THORSTEIN VEBLEN, *The Theory of the Leisure Class,*
vii, 167

ALTHOUGH *The Theory of the Leisure Class* is undoubtedly the most valuable contribution yet made to the philosophy of clothes, Veblen has been strangely neglected by our historians of fashion; his works contain a challenge which, in this country at all events, has been ignored. It is at once the purpose and the justification of this book to represent him, and with this end in view I have not hesitated to restate much that will be familiar to his readers. To these it will be obvious that, although I have attempted to develop and even to correct him in certain details, his teachings provide my point of departure. And I must further explain that I have found it best to expose his ideas as though they were my own and to reserve for a final chapter the discussion of those points at which there is a sensible divergence. It must, however, be said at once that no student of costume can possibly afford not to read and master *The Theory of the Leisure Class* and the posthumously published essay on dress in *Essays in Our Changing Order*.[1]

The economists, who have perhaps realised something of the greatness of Veblen, tend, I think, to neglect his theory of dress, and perhaps to see in the subject little save a vain peering into bonnet shops and haberdasheries, a vent for the interminable vapourings of Teufelsdröckh. The study of fashion does not quite lie within their province. It is a borderline science, important to the historian in that it exhibits in a pure form the changing impulse of social behaviour; to the artist in that here, if anywhere, we can trace a direct relationship between economics and aesthetics.

The charm of the study lies precisely in the ephemeral nature of the subject; in sociological studies fashion plays the role which has been allotted to *Drosophila*, the fruit fly, in the science of genetics. Here at a glance we can perceive phenomena so mobile in their response to varying effects, so rapid in their mutation that the deceptive force of inertia which overlays and obscures most other manifestations of human activity is reduced to a minimum.

The evidence is moreover abundant, not only without but within, for we have all experienced in our own persons the pains and pleasures of attire. When Veblen describes the needs of dress as "higher" or "spiritual", we can verify his assertion from our own experience. Who does not appreciate the expense, the inconvenience, perhaps even the discomfort of that which they feel them-

[1] Published by the Viking Press, New York, 1934.

selves compelled to wear? In obeying the fashion we undergo discomforts and distresses which are, from a strictly economic point of view, needless and futile. We do so for the sake of something which transcends our own immediate interests. What we may conveniently call our "baser nature" protests against the tyranny of tailors and dressmakers, but we are continually urged upwards and on by a sense of what is decent, correct, and comely, and though there are many who fail there are but few who will deliberately flout the categorical imperative of fashion.

Dress [says Lord Chesterfield] is a very foolish thing; and yet it is a very foolish thing for a man not to be well dressed, according to his rank and way of life; and it is so far from being a disparagement to any man's understanding, that it is rather a proof of it, to be as well dressed as those whom he lives with: the difference in this case, between a man of sense and a fop, is, that the fop values himself upon his dress; and the man of sense laughs at it, at the same time that he knows that he must not neglect it: there are a thousand foolish customs of this kind, which, not being criminal, must be complied with, and even cheerfully, by men of sense. Diogenes the Cynic was a wise man for despising them, but a fool for showing it.[1]

There is indeed a whole system of morality attached to clothes and more especially to fashion, a system different from, and, as we shall see, frequently at variance with that contained in our laws and our religion. To go to the theatre with five days' beard, to attend a ball in faultless evening dress (mark the adjective), but with your braces outside of, instead of within, your white waistcoat, to scatter ink on your spats, to reverse your tie, is not incompatible with the teachings of Our Saviour, nor does the written law take cognisance of the act. Nevertheless such behaviour will excite the strongest censure in "good" society. Far worse are those subtler forms of incorrect attire, the "wrong" tie, the bad hat,

[1] To his son, November 19th, 1745.

the "loud" skirt, or the flamboyant checks of the over-dressed vulgarian. Here the censure excited is almost exactly comparable to that occasioned by dishonourable conduct. I think it may be safely asserted that in many cases the condemnation of society at large is by no means so vehement as that supplied by the conscience of the individual himself, if he be made aware of his disgrace. Our clothes are too much a part of ourselves for us ever to be entirely indifferent to their condition; the feeling of being perfectly dressed imparts a buoyant confidence to the wearer, and it impresses the beholder as though the fabric were indeed a natural extension of the man. Nietzsche has said that a pretty woman, conscious of looking her best, never caught a cold however scanty her gown; the saying is poetically, if not literally, true. It is an undoubted fact that female prisoners, isolated from mankind, attempt to sustain their morale by the use of cosmetics; in the same way a uniform is known to exert a powerful effect upon conduct, and its careful upkeep is accounted a most important part of the duty of a soldier.[1]

So strong is the impulse of sartorial morality that it is difficult in praising clothes not to use such adjectives as "right", "good", "correct", "unimpeachable", or "fault-less", which belong properly to the discussion of conduct, while in discussing moral shortcomings we tend very naturally to fall into the language of dress and speak of a person's behaviour as being shabby, shoddy, threadbare, down at heel, botched, or slipshod.

It is pertinent, therefore, to ask to what extent the standards of sartorial morality conform to the other accepted standards of society. Now there can be no doubt that clothes can, and sometimes do, meet a certain number of strictly utilitarian needs. In colder climates

[1] Emerson reports a lady as saying: "A sense of being perfectly well dressed gives a feeling of inward tranquillity which Religion is powerless to bestow".

they control the temperature and in most climates they have through use become indispensable for this purpose. In the same way where once they have been established they become necessary to modesty. They may also be considered as an aid to beauty, both in the purest sense such as that which may lead a sculptor to prefer a clothed to a nude model, and also in the related sense of inspiring erotic emotion. Finally, they are of industrial utility and a vehicle for carrying instruments. Ideally it would be possible to design clothes capable of performing all these services, but it is very doubtful whether such clothes could ever become fashionable, for, as we shall see, the words "rational" and "utilitarian" have almost come to be words of abuse where dress is concerned; in the popular estimation industrially useful dress has seldom been accounted either beautiful or attractive. There would moreover be another objection to such utility wear; it would, if it were really useful, be infinitely various; for the tastes and needs of no two persons are quite similar. It is a commonplace that every society, and in some parts of the world every age, has its own style which is imposed upon a class or nation without reference to the needs of the individual. Nor do these standards provide even a generalised level of utility. Inevitably therefore the individual is required to sacrifice his personal comfort to the fashion, which, indeed, demands pecuniary, physiological, and aesthetic sacrifices, and often a deliberate flouting of public modesty. It is a fundamental law of dress that eccentricity be forbidden.

It will be seen therefore that a conflict must always exist between the utilitarian needs of the individual and what we can only call the futile[1] demands of sartorial morality.

---

[1] Futile only in the sense of being non-utilitarian and from an economic point of view wasteful, see Veblen, *The Theory of the Leisure Class*, p. 97 *et seq.*

In so far as the individual is concerned, the usual complaint arises from the great expense incurred in the business of being fashionably dressed, and, as Veblen points out in the passage cited above, much of that expense is incurred for objects which are wholly spiritual, for "respectability". But society, through its censors and its critics, is more various, more persistent, and more violent in its strictures; it is not only the expense but the very nature of dress which is condemned.

Moreover the Lord saith, Because the daughters of Zion are haughty, and walk with stretched forth necks and wanton eyes, walking and mincing as they go, and making a tinkling with their feet: Therefore the Lord will smite with a scab the crown of the head of the daughters of Zion, and the Lord will discover their secret parts. In that day the Lord will take away the bravery of their tinkling ornaments about their feet, and their cauls, and their round tires like the moon, the chains, and the bracelets, and the mufflers, the bonnets, and the ornaments of the legs, and the headbands, and the tablets, and the earrings, the rings, and nose jewels, the changeable suits of apparel, and the mantles, and the wimples, and the crisping pins, the glasses, and the fine linen, and the hoods, and the vails. And it shall come to pass, that instead of sweet smell there shall be stink; and instead of a girdle a rent; and instead of well set hair baldness; and instead of a stomacher a girding of sackcloth; and burning instead of beauty.[1]

There is no reason to suppose that Isaiah was the first moralist to make an attack upon finery. He had many imitators; the Church of Rome (who has herself shown remarkable talents as a modiste) was a persistent critic throughout the Middle Ages, and already in the sixth century St. Gregory of Tours was loud in his complaints.[2]

In this matter the doctors of the Church did but echo the politicians of the ancient world; sumptuary laws are

---

[1] Isaiah, iii, 16-24.      [2] See Max von Boehm, i, 182.

as old as Solon and extravagance is a constant theme of
Roman history.

> Nunc patimur longæ pacis mala, sævior armis
> Luxuria incubuit victumque ulcisctur orbem.[1]

As a rule, women have been the worst offenders in the
eyes of the critics, but by no means always; thus we find
that the French defeat at Crécy was ascribed by contemporary moralists to the indecency and extravagance
of the costume of the French nobility.[2]   In the same way
the Puritan criticism of fashionable dress in the seventeenth century was as much concerned with that of men
as with that of women.

Second in time, but not in vehemence, have been the
medical critics who saw in dress a danger to the body no
less great than that which had appeared to menace the
soul.   Ambroise Paré (1517–90) was perhaps one of the
first to exclaim at the practice of mortifying the flesh with
corsets of steel; there may easily have been others, for
tight lacing afflicted both sexes in the time of Petrarch.[3]
This has been the usual subject of medical criticism,
although very *décolleté* dresses have been condemned as
an invitation to pneumonia, and in the late nineteenth
and early twentieth centuries long trains were denounced
as being unhygienic.

Dress has ever been the despair of the political
economist and the administrator.   The fashions are
condemned because of their extravagance, because they
create industries only to destroy them, because they take
money out of the country, because they refuse to obey
any reasonable laws of supply and demand, because they
are inexplicable in terms of enlightened self-interest.
But since the Middle Ages the usual complaint, and that
which recurs again and again throughout history, is that

---

[1] Juvenal, *Satire* vi, 292.   See also Livy, xxx, 1-8.
[2] Max von Boehn, i, 218.          [3] *Ibid.* i, 192.

the fashion does not favour home industries. It is on this ground that legislators have usually sought to direct its course.

It is not until the nineteenth century that we find aesthetic criticism of the mode. Until then, or at least until the French Revolution, artists seem to have accepted the prevailing style with ease, even with enthusiasm. But in the middle of the last century aesthetes in this country, headed by G. F. Watts, R.A.,[1] began not only to criticise, but to attempt a positive movement of reform. At about the same time an independent attempt was made to rationalise dress; the reformers were later joined by humanitarians who objected to the use of certain kinds of plumage and fur. The latter movement achieved more than the former, which succeeded only in immortalising the name of Amelia Bloomer.

Finally it may be said that fashion has always been the butt of the humorist; its extravagances provoke his powers of caricature, his sense of fun, his indignation, his prurience. Every mode has been laughed at and abused in its time.

It need scarcely be pointed out that the protest and ridicule of the centuries has produced negligible results. The critics have been defeated again and again, always the fashion has worsted them. Nor has the style of dress changed in response to the opposition; we repeatedly find the satirists attacking a nascent mode which continues unaffected to its apogee, undeterred by the clamour it has provoked.

It may be said that these are but the trivial victories of an essentially trivial conflict, that the battle between bishops and the *beau monde* is, after all, but a trifling skirmish between old women and young ones, with no

[1] See the writings of G. F. Watts, III, vii, 202, *On Taste in Dress*, first published 1883.

bones broken and no one vitally affected. During the past two hundred years this has been pretty nearly the case, but from very early times until the emergence of modern capitalism every civilised country has enacted sumptuary laws for the preservation of morality and thrift, and above all for the maintenance of proper differences of rank in dress. In Europe since the beginning of the Middle Ages the number of these regulations has been prodigious. Attempts were made, first to restrain the consumer, and later, when that proved ineffectual, to regulate production. The penalties provided were severe, adequate provision was made for enforcing the laws, which were frequently voted by large majorities in the representative institutions of the age. Nothing was spared in the effort to curb the fashion. But the history of sumptuary laws is a history of dead letters.

The spectacle presented by the history of dress in Europe is therefore one of conflict between two inimical forces existing not only within the same societies but within the same persons (the legislators were frequently among the worst offenders). In that conflict the written sumptuary law and the unwritten laws of public opinion have usually been based upon all that we usually hold most precious in our civilisation: our religious and moral standards, our sense of decency and dignity, our concern for public health, our desire to see the lower orders kept in their proper place, our common sense, and our humanity. Nevertheless both public opinion and formal regulations are invariably set at naught; while Fashion, whose laws are imposed without formal sanctions, is obeyed with wonderful docility, and this despite the fact that her demands are unreasonable, arbitrary, and not infrequently cruel.

It is the enactment and enforcement of her laws which I shall attempt to examine.

# CHAPTER TWO

# SUMPTUOSITY

Il y a, dans les décisions de la mode et des femmes, une sorte de provocation au bon sens qui est charmante et qui ne peut fâcher que les esprits chagrins.

PAUL POIRET

AMORALITY of dress implies a set of values the presence or absence of which enables us to perceive whether a garment be "right" or "wrong". But here a confusion may arise, for, though any given article of clothing may be good in isolation, when displayed for instance upon the shelves of a museum, the same garment will be considered bad when placed in an unsuitable context. Thus, for instance, a smart headdress such as that illustrated in Plate 1 would be wholly wrong if worn with a bathing-dress at a Women's Institute today. Indeed the whole dress is obviously intended for one kind of occasion in one particular epoch. It will be found that specialisation, both in the sense of dress being permissible only for a given period and also in the sense of there being a multitude of contemporary styles for varying social occasions, has become more and more a characteristic of European costume throughout the past five hundred years. It is these two forms of context which concern us in studying the history of fashion. Here, however, I want to examine the merit of clothes in so far as it can be perceived in isolation from context, the virtue, that is to say, which resides in all fine clothes. For this I require a particular expression, for our notions of excellence in dress are so completely wedded to the

20

idea of change, of the latest, the most up-to-date thing, that we have hardly a word to describe the garments of all well-dressed people, both fashionable and unfashionable. To call the toga or the Mandarin's gown "chic" or "stylish" is to suggest a process of change which hardly existed in Rome or China; the clothes of the Beefeater or the Samurai are eminently respectable, but those who wear them are out of fashion; the tarboosh was never "all the go", for it has never gone.

What I refer to in this chapter as "Sumptuous Dress" is that which, whether fashionable, unfashionable, or out of fashion, has in one way or another provoked the respect and admiration of mankind; this, it must be noted, does not imply that the wearer has always been accounted in any sense equally respectable and admirable, for in certain cases we shall find that fine clothes are worn by one person in honour of another. It will be seen, therefore, that I am here considering the clothes, not only of those who belong to a privileged class and perform no menial tasks, but also of those who, without belonging to a privileged class, lead an ornamental, as distinct from an industrial existence, usually, though not always, as the ministers of some wealthy employer. In the former category we may place the wealthy and those whose position enables them to present the appearance of wealth; in the latter we find flunkeys and other expensive menials, soldiers, and, in a sense, priests. In modern society many persons belong to both groups and adopt their appropriate costumes occasionally.

Now the obvious common quality of all these classes is their wealth or the wealth that is spent upon them; whatever form their costume may take it will always be indicative thereof. But the manner in which wealth is displayed upon the person is often very oblique and by no means apparent at first sight; it is here that the analysis of what Veblen calls "Pecuniary Canons of Taste" is of the utmost value. Veblen has expressed the modes of pecuniary taste under three headings: *Conspicuous Consumption*, *Conspicuous Leisure*, and *Conspicuous Waste*, and to these I would add a fourth which I will call *Conspicuous Outrage*. To understand the nature of Sumptuous Dress we must glance at each of these categories, without which, indeed, the history of fashion is not explicable.

*Conspicuous Consumption.*—The simplest and most obvious manner of displaying wealth is to take the greatest possible number of valuable objects and attach them to the wearer's person. "A fully equipped Santal belle carries two anklets, and perhaps twelve bracelets, and a necklace weighing a pound, the total weight of ornaments on her person amounting to thirty-four pounds of bell metal—a greater weight", says Captain Sherwell, "than one of our drawing-room belles could well lift. We may without much exaggeration say with Grosse that primitive man attaches to his body all the ornaments he can get, and that he adorns all the parts of his body that can bear an ornament." [1] The practice is not extinct, though it has, as we shall see, undergone substantial modification. Moreover, this method of displaying wealth is comparable to the large-scale advertisements that are set upon hoardings; the intention is to astonish and to impress the world at large. It is a method unsuited to a society in which persons of the same class meet in privacy and in which a certain income is taken for granted. Thus we find that, at a time when monarchs lived very much in the presence of a very unsophisticated public, the wearing of full regalia was much commoner than today, when it is reserved for specially large crowds

[1] I have lifted this passage with its quotations entire from Westermarck's *History of Human Marriage*, i, xv, 498.

*PLATE 2*

Conspicuous Consumption

on specially important occasions. Conspicuous Consumption persists in the ceremonies of the older Churches, on the music-hall stage, the cinema, and in military evolutions of a very public character. It is also found, though in a modified form, where individuals have achieved wealth in very humble surroundings. But if the ornate costume intended for the admiration of the vulgar be transferred to a higher stratum of society, it will itself be accounted vulgar or "loud". It is indeed the special glory of the good Savile Row tailor that he achieves an effect of great expense by his very lack of flamboyance; the perfection of his cut is manifested in its extreme discretion.

Nevertheless, a certain minimal display of wealth is essential; no excellence of cut, hue, or design will serve to redeem the sin of poverty. A cheap material cannot please, only "good" materials are permissible, and these must be expensively worked. The "good" tailor-made, that is to say the expensive material worked by hand, is always worthy of respect. In the same way nothing can compensate for the lack of "real" materials, *real* pearls, *real* silk, *real* lace, etc. In other words, the materials employed must be difficult to obtain or laborious to produce. The same standard is applied in the costume of many European peasants; here the merit of the artifact resides, not in the value of the materials employed, but in the enormous amount of socially necessary labour time which has been devoted to the production; careful and laborious handicraft of this kind commands almost universal admiration, we are astonished and delighted by the enormous amount of work "put into" the manufacture of these garments.

A subtler form of conspicuous consumption consists in the exhibition of more than one of the garments worn. Thus we find the practice of looping up the skirts of a dress in order to show a costly underskirt beneath, of "slashing" a garment to the same end, or again, more discreetly, of wearing rustling petticoats, the presence of which may be advertised only by a susurrus, or by lining the skirt with some brilliant material which will flare as the wearer passes.

The display of linen has been a feature of masculine dress since the end of the Middle Ages and has frequently been used in feminine apparel; linen has a particular value as an indication of wealth, in that it betrays dirt at once and must be frequently renewed. The pattern of masculine dress during the past three hundred years has been two or more coverings cut away in stages to display a shirt. In the mid-seventeenth century the effect was enhanced by the provision of a hiatus between the waistcoat and the breeches; here the shirt bellied out again as though to guarantee its continuity at all levels.

Within recent years conspicuous consumption has been demonstrated in dress much as it is in old masters; the signature of the maker, always provided that his prices were sufficiently high, was deemed sufficient to redeem all other defects. As a natural consequence unscrupulous dealers were able to exploit the public by affixing a Parisian mark to a work of inferior quality; the public was usually quite unable to detect the fraud.

*Conspicuous Leisure.*—The mere demonstration of purchasing power is the simplest device of sumptuosity; much more important is that which Veblen calls 'Conspicuous Leisure', that is to say the demonstration of an honourably futile existence, one that is so far removed from menial necessities that clothes can be worn which impede physical labour. Dress of this kind marks the wearer at once as a member of the Leisure Class, one who can exist without working and who is, therefore, demonstrably in receipt of a certain income. We admire such clothes almost instinctively, feeling them to be elegant and dignified, belonging, as it were, to a world in which the wolf has been kept far from the door. It is indeed doubtful if we can conceive of dignity without a certain degree of leisure, and undoubtedly, if we attempt to personify that quality in a graphic form, we shall find that some measure of repose is essential both in the attitude and the clothes of our subject.

Examples of the exhibition of leisure through clothes are abundant, indeed the history of fashion is to a large extent the history thereof. Thus the sumptuous hat has nearly always been devised, either to give no protection to the head, or to make the wearer helpless in a high wind, or to blind her with its brim, while the hair or wig can be raised to a precarious height, or given an appearance of crushing weight as in the chignon. Women's hats and hair have for long been a jest among men, but both sexes have displayed their leisure in this manner; one has only to look at the hats of the mediaeval gentleman, at the periwig, or indeed at the top hat.

Collars also have frequently been devised so as to give the wearer an elegant appearance of being strangled. The ruff of the fifteenth and sixteenth centuries is one example, the epicene choker collar of the early twentieth century another.

The arm and hand have been incapacitated as a demonstration of exemption from manual labour by means of long trailing sleeves, sleeves of episcopal grandeur, very tight, or so fashioned as to project well beyond the hand. The hand itself must be most carefully tended, the nails being pointed, lacquered, and/or kept scrupulously clean and soft; rings and bracelets help to sustain its genteel appearance, while gloves give further evidence of leisure.[1]

The constriction of the waist, which has at various periods included a substantial deformation of the thorax and the hips, is clearly not only a substantial impediment to useful work but to the health upon which such work depends. Corsets, at their most violent, crush in the ribs, constrict the vitals, deform the spine, and, by interfering with the digestive processes, induce that eminently genteel disorder, the vapours. In comparatively recent times the slender waist, diminished by the padded bulk of breasts and buttocks, has been accounted something eminently feminine and fragile; as we have already noticed, both sexes have submitted to tight lacing, though it is certainly in women's clothes that the practice has been most enduring, being indeed almost a constant characteristic of the dress of European women.

Skirts also are a symbol of dignified leisure in both sexes and they will be found in one form or another in most civilisations. At a very early date they were held to distinguish the civilised man from the barbarian; they remain the dress of priests in the older Churches. It is only in very poor circumstances, as for instance in Belgian industry and Swiss agriculture, that trousers have been the accepted dress of European women.[2] In themselves, when extended to the ground, skirts provide an excellent guarantee of immobility; but their effect is increased by the train, a peculiar symbol of dignity, by lateral extension as a further impediment to free movement,

[1] "It cannot be in good taste to squeeze it (the hand) into a glove so much too small for it that it becomes useless for any purpose beyond holding a visiting card, the division of the fingers extending only down to the middle of the hand knuckle, and the back and inside of the hand pinched into shapelessness and uselessness. Though the hand is not permanently injured by the tight glove as the foot is by the tight shoe, the effect is ignoble and absurd." G. F. Watts, *op. cit.*

[2] See W. M. Webb, *The Heritage of Dress*, pp. 78-80.

and by constriction as in the hobble, which binds the legs together (see Plates 10 and 13).

Perhaps the most effectual guarantee of social standing is obtained by means of unpractical footwear. Of China we will speak later, but in Europe the high-heeled shoe has been an almost constant phenomenon; it is a most effectual symbol of leisure and a great favourite with the theorists; we shall have much to say regarding it. It has been worn by both sexes, but has become a particularly enduring symbol of feminine inertia. It is interesting to notice to what extent the weight of poetical tradition conspires to place women upon this particular pedestal. Big solid feet, however beautifully formed, are definitely unromantic, so too are stout workmanlike boots, clogs, or brogues. It is felt to be poetically appropriate that the heroine, whose ugly sisters had condemned her to a socially useful existence, should gain her prince by means of her atrophied toes. The glass slipper is not only a means of identification, but a certificate of economic inefficiency. We feel it to be right and proper that Cinderella should be translated from the scullery to the throne.

Fashions in men's footwear do nowadays permit a certain glossy serviceability (to be abandoned on ceremonial occasions), but the pointed shoes of the Middle Ages (see Plate 3) and the heelless slippers of the Turk are quite as unpractical as any feminine mode. In the same way a great variety of men's boots are so designed that though a man can ride in them he may hardly walk.

Finally we may notice that kind of dress which may be called "difficult". It is of two kinds: that which like the kilt or toga requires some art in adjustment; secondly, and this is much more common, the kind of dress which has obviously been fastened upon the wearer by an

27

attendant. The latter is the more certainly a dress of conspicuous leisure.

Enough has been said perhaps to suggest that the sumptuously dressed person is no sybarite. He or she is a person who goes to great expense and pains to mortify the flesh. It must, moreover, be borne in mind that the leisurely existence suggested by costume is by no means always a reality. The black-coated, well-starched clerk who runs to catch the train with the temperature at 98° in the shade, and his sister who endures the agony of high heels and bare legs in a blizzard, are frequently very industrious persons, but their social pretensions, perhaps even their livelihood, demand a decent standard of discomfort in their dress.

Fortunately there are limiting factors which prevent any fashion from being pushed beyond a certain point. Clothes must always be a graceful encumbrance; to exhibit awkwardness argues an inability to deal with the paraphernalia of polite existence suggestive of a plebeian lack of experience. It is, moreover, important to notice that exaggeration finishes by defeating its own ends; as an extension of the person, clothes must remain in proportion thereto; if they dwarf the body the effect of dignity is diminished. A train two yards long is impressive, a train forty yards long grotesque.[1] Again, any undue exaggeration of the prevailing mode is somewhat like the display of easily convertible wealth upon the person; it is something intended for the multitude and therefore vulgar.

*Conspicuous Waste.*—A further mitigation of the law of conspicuous leisure is obtained by the existence of certain diversions and occupations which are socially acceptable, and this brings us to the consideration of Conspicuous Waste. Conspicuous Waste is in truth a refinement of

[1] See Flugel, *The Psychology of Clothes*, pp. 36-7.

28

Conspicuous Leisure (students of Veblen will notice that I am here making free with his theories). It is, as it were, the overflow of energy from the simpler forms of sumptuous display; it is not a characteristic of dress, but an important determinant in their fashioning.

It is a well-known fact that in all primitive religious ceremonies, as also in primitive burial customs, a certain amount of wealth is destroyed or interred in honour of the gods or heroes. In early times these are followed to the grave by their belongings, and in Egypt a quite enormous amount of furnishing was provided for the dead. Elaborate and expensive funerals are a notable item of expenditure even among the very poor in this country, even where considerable sacrifices are involved. The charm of expensive mourning is that it is money thrown away, no return can be expected, it is one of the most conspicuous forms of waste.

> And when they buried him the little port
> Had seldom seen a costlier funeral.

Now the use of mourning and the consumption of funeral bakemeats is but an occasional and special form of conspicuous waste. From those whose lives are entirely or largely divorced from productive labour much more is required. Somehow they must contrive to kill time in occupations which, however active, are patently futile. Economically their lives must be a perpetual burial thereof and their clothes a decent mourning. Thus we have the noble occupations, those which are completely non-profit-making and, from the point of view of the well-being of the community, wholly futile. Of these the chief, and to the historian of fashion the most important, are war and sport. Little less noble are what we may call the genteel occupations, i.e. those which involve a minimum of bodily exertion. Some of these approach so nearly to futility as to be accounted noble, for instance those nominally administrative functions which involve hardly anything save the adoption of a distinctive costume; also worship where it is a whole-time job, and particularly when the income derived therefrom seems to be out of all proportion to the services rendered; diplomacy and the law have also been accounted sufficiently genteel to make of their uniforms a token of honour.

Of lesser importance are such occasional vehicles for the expenditure of unprofitable energy as worship, gambling, dancing, etc., which are not in the nature of a whole-time job, and which, though usually the occasion for a display of finery, have no very distinctive uniform. In this category we may place that kind of sporting activity which consists simply in attending sporting events.

The importance of war and sport to the student of dress lies in the fact that these occupations have at various times been the chief and almost the only active employment of an entire caste or class, and that they have the double advantage of being not only largely unprofitable but also very expensive. No pains have been spared to make them more so, and although some of the items of expense are of course utilitarian, in the sense of being intended to promote the more efficient prosecution of the campaign or chase, others are purely futile and exist only "that the thing may be done in style". It is very possible that no part of the fighting man's equipment or training is without a utilitarian origin, and that this is true even of the Papal Guards; but it can hardly be denied that in many armies sartorial and ceremonial observances, the practical utility of which have long been forgotten, have been accounted of greater moment than the quality of food or weapons,[1] so that one is at

---

[1] It should, however, be noted that not all military services are equally respectable; they vary, not according to the degree of courage required, but according to

times led to doubt whether the primary object of armies
be not to provide a magnificent setting for conspicuous
waste rather than to implement the policies of nations.
In the same way it is not thought unreasonable, but
rather glorious, that the most English of sports should
consist in the pursuit of an inedible animal, with an
expensive pack of hounds, a great assembly of sumptu-
ously dressed ladies and gentlemen, and a stiff bill for
damages at the end. "The image of war, without its
guilt, and only five and twenty per cent of its danger."
The influence of these two noble occupations has been
such that at different moments in the history of modern
Europe the costume of a gentleman has, with very little
modification, been that of an officer or a sportsman.

*Conspicuous Outrage.*—So far we have dealt only with the
exhibition of pecuniary strength through the display of
wealth and leisure; there is, however, another characteristic of sumptuous, and especially of fashionable dress,
which must be mentioned. It is the aim of fashionable
people in certain social conditions to show their indifference, not only to vulgar needs, but also to vulgar
ideas. It is a thing that we recognise more easily in the
manners, language, and morals of the fashionable world
than in its dress. We may discern two elements therein:
(1) the esoteric, (2) the defiant. The esoteric element
is commonly expressed in the form of a special jargon,
slang, or pronunciation, as for instance in the use of
"pink", "scarlet", "brush", "hounds", etc., in the hunt-
ing field, in the use of French or the dead languages
in conversation, of Christian names or diminutives for
socially reputable people, and of certain methods of
pronunciation in such proper names as Derby, Bertram,
Leveson-Gower, etc. The defiant note is struck by the

the amount of manual work involved; thus pioneers have always been of little
account, while the cavalry comes first in fashionable repute.

use of obscene language, by the abandonment of refinements of speech which have been vulgarised, by an affected cynicism or piety, and by the rejection of vulgar standards of morality, particularly in matters of sexual behaviour.

In clothes conspicuous outrage usually takes the form of an affront to prudery. Thus in the Middle Ages it was thought shocking in a woman to show her hair ("for if the woman be not covered, let her also be shorn"[1]). As a result the coiffure of the time shows a more and more complete exposure of the hair. A somewhat similar process was at work in women's bonnets in the 'forties and 'fifties of the last century. But the obvious example of this tendency is the exposure of the arms, bosom, and legs. The concealment of the person, or such portions thereof as happen to be taboo, is a function of dress, fashionable and unfashionable. Anthropologists tell us that this concealment is inextricably involved with the opposite business of display. Clothes, in so far as they are an instrument of modesty and not of climatic protection, would seem to have originated as a banner or advertisement of the pudenda. Such races as go naked are by no means deficient in modesty, and the first garments worn were perhaps used in erotic dances as a means to excitement; they conserve this quality even when they have become daily wear, and, through being customary, become a necessary aid to decency and of magical importance. They may then be compared to a beribboned chocolate box or gilded shrine serving to enhance the value of that which might, if exposed to view, be held too cheap. That it is characteristic of sumptuous dress to unite concealment and exposure in a marked degree is a truth which need scarcely be

---

[1] St. Paul, 1 Corinthians, xi, 6. See also von Boehn, i, 206, and Ruppert, *Histoire du Costume de l'antiquité au xix<sup>e</sup> siècle*, I, 50-52.

emphasised. Where fashions have originated in the colder climates display is almost always carried to greater lengths by the upper classes than by their social inferiors.

It will be realised that the outrageous quality of dress does not necessarily depend upon the actual baring of the body. Anyone who has spent the morning painting from a nude model and then seen her go out to lunch with a friend will know in what manner clothes serve, not only to cover the figure, but to improve its shape, to extend and to enlarge it in the desired directions, to correct its proportions, thus bringing them into harmony with the prevailing canons of taste. Clothes generalise the shape of the body, reduce it to a more geometrical form and suggest a classical perfection of outline which is rare in nature, and this is eminently a property of many forms of sumptuous dress.

Sexual display in that type of sumptuous dress which may truly be called fashionable is for ever changing under the influence of two opposite but inseparable forces. Modesty itself is not tied to a fixed and immutable canon, but would seem rather to depend upon conventions which vary from place to place and from time to time. Thus we have seen in our own time women's legs, which were once things to be covered at all costs, made quite familiar and proper as they have long been among certain savage tribes. Again the modern minimal bathing-dress is not felt to be shocking on the beach, but would be so considered at a tea-party. To the Chinese an exposure of the feet is very gross, while to Mahommedans it is of little account compared to that of the face. In short: immodesty is a breach of custom, and where customs do not change there is no great immodesty in dress. But with us the fashion seizes now on one member, now on another and displays it as far as may be. Fashionable exposure begins by shocking the vulgar, but it ends by establishing itself as a custom and thus ceasing to shock; its failure is implicit in its success. But so long as there is a development of the mode the quality of outrage is maintained.

Finally opinion can in certain cases be outraged by the acceptance of a new aesthetic standard to which the public is as yet unaccustomed. Just as the exhibition of the person marks an immunity to vulgar morality, so does the exhibition of esoteric ideas mark a superiority to vulgar notions; the object would appear to be in both cases the same, to show one's attachment to an informed and superior class.

In this account of sumptuous dress the reader will probably discover many omissions. We have, for instance, said nothing of those symbols which are so important in clothing, as for instance the "old school tie" which to the initiate is as eloquent of the wearer's sojourn as is the broad arrow of the convict. Nevertheless we have, I think, accomplished the preliminaries necessary to a study of finery. It must be repeated that in considering the essential virtues of dress we have in truth done no more than analyse one central phenomenon. In each case we come back to the basic question of expenditure. Conspicuous consumption is but the putting of wealth upon the person, conspicuous leisure the demonstration of a wealthy ease, and conspicuous waste of wealthy activity. Our feelings concerning the right spending of money on dress are, however, so blended with other emotions, our sense of beauty, martial glamour, sexual desirability, etc., that it is not easy to disentangle one factor from the other. It is difficult for us to tell to what extent those standards which Veblen calls the "pecuniary canons of taste" affect our judgment. And yet it is surely just that nice

34

perception of financial worth which makes the difference between the civilised man and the barbarian. On the face of it, it may seem that the bejewelled lady of Europe differs little from the savage with her necklace of beads. But although a diamond cross upon the bosom of a young beauty serves all the purposes of a Moroccan charm, leading us, in the one case, as in the other, to think well of the person, the principles, and the aspect of the wearer, the effect will be totally marred in *our* eyes if the ornament be a tawdry and vulgar thing of glass in "atrociously vulgar taste". It will indeed be condemned as "barbarian". Our sense of value cannot ever be quite divorced from our sense of cost or class.

In conclusion a word should be said regarding the accessories of sumptuous dress. Costume does not end with what is worn and may even be held to extend to the interior decoration, the architecture, the habits of speech, the ideas, and all the other belongings of a people in so far as they assist in producing the desired effect of sumptuosity. I must, however, confine myself to those portable belongings which are definitely intended to subserve the costume. They will on the whole be found to exhibit conspicuous leisure. The handkerchief which is too small for use, the fan which does not refresh, the hypertrophied muff, the unnecessary stick, etc. Perhaps the most interesting accessory of fashion is the domestic, or rather the ornamental, animal. The laws regulating the use of animals for sumptuous purposes are the same as those which govern the use of clothes; expense and futility are the criteria. Although the number of species which has been pressed into service is enormous, it will hardly ever be found that these are of an outstandingly useful kind. Sheep, pigs, ducks, hens, or goats seldom become household pets or the ornaments of a gentleman's garden, while deer will be more welcome in his park than cows or any save the most expensive horses. Preference is given to exotics such as parrots and canaries, monkeys, tortoises, goldfish, and other futile and largely inedible animals. The cat is an exception, although even here those varieties which are more expensive than useful will be preferred.

The comparison between the cat and the dog is highly instructive. The cat is the most polite of the domestic animals. Its life in the home is almost a kind of symbiosis. It is very clean in its habits; on the whole it pays its way and is frequently of more service than disservice to its owner.

The dog on the other hand has not shown the cat's adaptation to the life of cities; he belongs to the kennel, but is seldom found there when used as an ornament. As Veblen points out: "He is the filthiest of the domestic animals in his person and the nastiest in his habits. For this he makes up in a servile attitude towards his master, and a readiness to inflict damage and discomfort on all else."[1]

The enormous esteem in which dogs are held and their almost universal employment as ornaments is no doubt in a large measure due to this servile attitude; also perhaps they are psychological substitutes for children (a large section of the pet-loving public in this country consists of women in the higher income groups). But what makes dogs modish above all other creatures is (a) their connection with the futile pursuits of the chase, (b) their sequacity which makes them in effect a part of the costume, (c) and this is their greatest merit, the extreme malleability of the species when subjected to selective breeding. Dogs are the fashion because we can fashion them to our will. Dogs, much more than cats, can be made objects of conspicuous leisure; they can

[1] *The Theory of the Leisure Class,* p. 141.

be rendered completely incapable of fending for themselves and made demonstrable objects of continual expense and care (whoever saw a cat wearing a little coat in the cold weather?) The highly-bred dog can have its whole frame twisted and distorted into shapes of the most astonishing kind. An uninstructed observer would suppose that the owners and vendors of these crippled and unhealthy animals must of necessity be exceedingly cruel. On being further informed that the monstrosity fanciers are amongst the most resolute critics of vivisection he would set them down as hypocrites. Such accusations would, however, be unjust; the torturers are genuinely devoted to their victims. Fashion, as we have said, has a morality of its own; and the cruelty involved in the deformation of unoffending animals, like that involved in blood sports, is redeemed by the economic futility of the motive; that involved in scientific experiments is felt to be odious because of its unpardonable utility.

# CHAPTER THREE

# FASHION

As good be out of the world as out of fashion.[1]

COLLEY CIBBER

IN discussing the merits of any costume, no contextual factor is more important, or at times more misleading, than that of the changing fashion. Dress which is sumptuous, but not fashionable, is fairly easily explained by an application of Veblen's theories, but that which is in a perpetual state of flux and so unstable that, in the course of a few decades, every manifestation of sumptuosity is transformed, constitutes a problem mysterious in itself and vital to our entire argument.

For us, fashion is the essential virtue without which all is vain. We may, under certain circumstances, allow the merit of certain dresses which do not pretend to novelty, but that which is *démodé*, or which attempts, and yet fails, to be in vogue is damned without further discussion. We are indeed such creatures of fashion that we tend to accept its influence almost as a law of nature, a tendency which has been the undoing of many theorists. To avoid making any such mistake it may be as well to begin this chapter by examining a department in the history of dress wherein the influence of fashion has been so slight as to be barely perceptible; thereby we may be better able to place the phenomenon of fashion historically and geographically, to examine some of its attendant phenomena; and finally, in the light of these facts to approach the problem of its causation.

[1] But see Appendix B

Now the most obvious and convenient antithesis to the dress of the western world is that of China; not that we cannot find many similar examples of a static mode, but in that ancient civilisation we have the oldest continuous culture of mankind, one which has developed apart from our own, and one which has pushed the art of living and the applied arts to a degree of perfection to which we in the West have but recently approached.

China has produced sumptuous dress which is very similar to that of the West in that it is a dress of conspicuous leisure. The long silk robe of the mandarin, with its projecting sleeves designed to frustrate manual labour and its high stiff collar, is quite western in its leisurely nature. So too is the habit of allowing one or more of the finger nails to grow to a prodigious length as an advertisement of the scholarly life. The more extravagant forms of sumptuosity are rare; gaudiness is a Manchu rather than a Chinese characteristic. The refinement of the Chinese, like that of western man during the past 150 years, tends towards a sober "goodness" in quality. In most respects the clothes of women resemble those of men, the same robe and trousers (in the North at least) and the same sobriety of taste, with this important distinction: where Europeans have demonstrated conspicuous leisure by binding the waist the Chinese have bound the foot and this has been done with great thoroughness for many generations. Until very recent times the Celestial lady tottered painfully upon feet which had been mutilated in early youth, and was thus, theoretically, debarred from almost any task of social utility. As in Europe, so in China, protests were made. Several scholars of the eighteenth and early nineteenth centuries assailed the practice, which was indeed forbidden by a law of the emperor Kang-Hsi.[1]

[1] See Wieger, *Moral Tenets and Customs of the Chinese*, p. 189.

The Manchu ladies did not at first bind their feet nor did the practice become general amongst them; it must be remembered that they were of a ruling caste, nevertheless the emperor Chien Lung found it necessary to forbid them to follow the Chinese custom. The empress dowager also attempted, and failed, to abolish the practice.

It will be seen that the sumptuous dress of China bears a great similarity to that of Europe in that it is a dress of conspicuous leisure, but it differs in two important respects: it is modest,[1] and it is static.

Chinese erotic imagination has played upon the atrophied foot, but this was unseen both in life and in decent art. So too was every other part of the body save for the face and hands; by this I do not simply mean that the person was clothed, but that the form was in no way emphasised. In no age have the Chinese exhibited those members upon which the European mind has at one time or another dwelt with loving curiosity; there, all is muffled or suppressed by a waving formless garment.[2] The nearest approach to the Chinese practice to be found in the West is in the dress of the Spanish women of the late sixteenth century, the invisible foot, the shape of the body masked and deformed by its dress, the breasts weighted down to flatness with leaden plates, just as they are flattened by the chest-binding jacket, only the face and hands visible. Here, however, the resemblance ends. If Europe had worshipped the foot as China has, more and more of it would have been revealed to us, increasingly daring modes would have come into vogue, until the "erogenous zone" had shifted elsewhere. In China the bound foot became fashionable, if one can use such a word of Chinese dress, as the result of a very long

[1] See Robert K. Douglas, *Society in China*, xxii, 361.
[2] See Lin Yu Tang, *My Country and My People*, Part II.

and gradual process which culminated in the tenth
century and remained static until the irruption of western
fashions which have played havoc with those of the Far
East.[1]

The bound foot, the tartar head-dress, and the pigtail
excepted, we may almost say that the Chinese and his
family have remained unaltered in outward appearance
since the classical age.[2]   It is as though we in Europe
had made no very essential change in our dress since the
Punic Wars.   Except perhaps for Egyptian dress which
underwent considerable modifications after the XVIIIth
Dynasty, and Roman dress, which shows a slow but
sensible development, this has been the nature of all
dress, savage and civilised, in every part of the world
untouched by European influence.   That is to say that
so long as a culture has maintained itself, its own particular form of dress has persisted without any very
noticeable change, or at all events without any change
comparable to that which we have seen during the past
five hundred years in Europe, or indeed to the changes in
women's dress which have taken place within the present
century.

When therefore we speak of fashions in dress we refer
to a phenomenon of comparatively recent origin.   Its
beginnings were so gradual that it is impossible to say
at what point the machine really starts into motion, but
the process can hardly be said to have been at work in the
time of Charlemagne and was definitely active by the
beginning of the thirteenth century; from then onwards
the rate of change increases until in our own times it has

---

[1] The importance of Chinese dress to any philosophy of clothes is not generally
realised even today.   Thus of all the wise and witty generalisations concerning
"Man" and "Woman" made by Willet Cunnington in his book, *Why Women
Wear Clothes*, few if any will hold good if the Chinese be admitted to membership
of the human race.

[2] See Williams, *A Short History of China*, i, 14.

41

become prodigious. Simultaneous with the increase in pace goes an increase in scope; first the nobility, then the burghers, then the craftsmen are involved, until finally, in industrialised societies, such as Britain and the United States, fashion dominates the entire population almost without exception. With the increase in social depth goes an increase in diffusion; European fashions have accompanied European enterprise and have established themselves throughout the habitable world. There has also been a development, though of a less even character, towards increased centralisation. At times the different capitals of Europe, and notably Madrid, Venice, Brussels, Florence, Vienna, London, and Paris, had each their own fashion or variants thereof, but the two last have become to an increasing extent the dominating centres.[1]

To these platitudes, which form a necessary part of any introduction to a theory of fashion, we must add three more concerning the manner in which fashion has developed.

(1) Although the rate of change has not been even, and there have been moments of catastrophic development, there is never any complete break in the fashion; fashions are never created, always they evolve. Usually it will be found that a form of garment develops gradually to a greater and greater distortion, and then disappears fairly rapidly. In men's dress, and in particular in the dress of soldiers, we can frequently perceive atrophied members. In the contemporary (1939) work of a London tailor there are buttons, flaps, and incisions as useless and as historically interesting as the male nipple

---

[1] But see Willet Cunnington: "It is a curious error to suppose that English women accept their fashions from Paris"; any similarity, he thinks, results simply from a chance identity of mental attitude—*Feminine Attitudes of the 19th Century*, p. 16. Doubtless there has been a process of selection and adaptation, but in fact London has shopped in Paris and not vice versa. The substantial similarity of the two fashions is much greater than can be accounted for by the explanation proposed.

or the appendix. To take one example from many, the hatband, both that which we find outside nearly all hats, and that which persists within some, was formerly useful in keeping the stuff of the head-dress upon the head, as in the Arab head-dress of today. On a modern felt hat it has entirely lost its original use; the band is sewn onto the side of the crown; no one would think of untying the bow, but the maddest of hatters would not dream of omitting it.[1] In women's dress, which nowadays is far less conservative than that of men, the retention of archaic features is less noticeable; nevertheless here too we do find a similar process at work, but in the opposite direction; thus the hatband, instead of being atrophied suffers hypertrophy; it becomes a brilliant decorative motive, an excuse for streamers or a large bow. Broadly speaking we may say that conservatism in dress consists in this: utilitarian features are retained, but only on condition that they lose their utility; they are transformed into vehicles for the demonstration of conspicuous consumption. Another example, that of the safety-pin, may serve to show how a given object can evolve two varieties. Crude but recognisable safety-pins can be found at a very early period of history; at this stage the thing is both useful and ornamental, being frequently made of bronze or gold. It has subsequently developed in both directions; first into the conspicuous brooch which commonly has no safety guard, secondly into the very practical modern safety-pin; this latter is hidden away from public gaze, and to wear it upon the person as a fastening to the dress is thought very ignominious.

(2) In non-European Ancient and Mediaeval dress

[1] See W. M. Webb, *The Heritage of Dress* (London, 1907). Webb produces a great number of examples besides the two which I cite here, but he deals only with atrophy: in consequence pays little attention to survivals in feminine dress.

the distinction between the sexes is not always very marked. The robe, the train, the long hair, and big headdress, which are still to be found in the archaic dress of priests and officials, make it at times difficult to tell men from women. The division of humanity into breeched and petticoated sections is not complete even in the sixteenth century, and the tendency for one sex to copy the other persists, though with decreasing force. Thus we find many epicene fashions such as the ruff, the high-heeled shoe, and the wig. It is not until the nineteenth century that the separation is made complete, and even then we can find many reflected fashions[1] (see Plate 3).

(3) Finally we may notice the tendency towards increased specialisation. There have always been special dresses and decorations for special occasions: war paint, canonicals, regalia, etc., but the provision of special attire for almost every activity and its spread to larger and larger classes of people is, I think, a distinctively western development. Thus, for instance, what was formerly a specifically ceremonial attire had, by the nineteenth century, become evening dress and a particular vehicle of sumptuosity, with its own peculiar standard of feminine modesty; a specific war dress, as distinct from armour, was evolved in the seventeenth and eighteenth centuries, and a specific sports dress, again with its own standard of modesty, in the twentieth. Today special types of garment exist for all the different sports and sporting occasions, as also for walking, riding, dancing, drinking cocktails, etc.[2]

[1] It is important to distinguish between epicene fashions such as those noted above, which developed simultaneously upon both sexes, and borrowed fashions: that is garments imitated from those of the opposite sex. Numerous examples of the latter will be found in C. Willet Cunnington's *English Women's Clothes in the Nineteenth Century.*

[2] Willet Cunnington, however, is of the opinion that on balance the number and variety of occasional dresses has decreased since the nineteenth century. (*Why Women Wear Clothes,* p. 260.)

PLATE 3

15th century: *Presentation in the Temple* by the Master of *The Life of the Virgin*

Note the conspicuously leisurely clothes worn by both sexes, the sleeves worn by
the fourth man from the right whose whole dress is by 20th century standards
"feminine", and the pointed shoes

It will be seen that the development of fashion is a process considerably wider in scope than the mutation of various types of garment. But even if we look at it only from this restricted point of view, it is clear that it is not just a factor in our dress but an over all determinant. Under the influence of fashion we have, in the course of 140 years, seen women completely change the shape and texture of their garments; they have during a period of four generations contrived to look like milk churns, like spinning-tops, like inverted flowers, and like boys. The whole make of their clothes, and, as it would appear, of their bodies has been changed, not once but half a dozen times, under the varying impulse of fashion. In society as we know it in the West, fashion may fairly be described as the element in which clothes change and have their being. Of the many factors which go to the design and use of dress—protection, convenience, sexual advertisement, beauty, and those which we have described as being characteristically sumptuous—all are influenced and dominated by the prevailing mode; the demands of convenience and protection are restrained, the form taken by sexual display directed hither and thither about the person, and the specifically sumptuous characteristics enlarged, altered, or abolished by this immanent force. As the climate is to fauna, so is fashion to dress, and even the consciously archaistic clothes of the noble professions and the theatre are not immune to its influence.

What then sets the evolutionary process into motion, maintains and increases its velocity, gives it its tremendous force and accounts for its connected phenomena? The historians tend to be vague upon this point; they produce secondary factors of undeniable importance, but insufficient to supply a complete answer. Resolute attempts to produce a theory of fashion are rare; of

Veblen's account (which is not mine) I will speak later; here it may be useful to discuss other systems which, though they appear to me to be radically unsound, are by no means unilluminating or without value. These may be said, roughly speaking, to fall into four main groups: (1) those which explain the changes of fashion as the work of a few individuals; (2) those which see in fashion a product of human nature; (3) those which see in it a reflection of great political or spiritual events; (4) those which invoke the authority of a Higher Power.

Very few writers on fashion see in the action of individuals the principal cause of fashionable change, nevertheless the view is fairly widespread that certain people, and notably the "leaders" who set the fashion or the business men who "create" it, are of primary importance.

Obviously no history of dress would be complete without mention of Beau Brummel or Mlle de Fontanges; that these, and others, were monarchs is indisputable; but to conceive of them as despots is, I am sure, to put the cart before the horse.[1] The leader of fashion does not come into existence until the fashion is itself created and, though he may vary the development thereof in details, he does not do so in essentials; he does not create, he adapts. A king or person of great social eminence may indeed lead the fashion, but he leads only in the general direction which it has already adopted.

No leader has ever succeeded in stopping the evolutionary process. The thing was tried by one of the most fashionable of our monarchs and failed utterly. In 1666, we, being then at war with France, decided to cease taking our mode from Versailles and to adopt a form of masculine attire which would be genteel,

---

[1] See Fischel and von Boehn, *Modes and Manners of the XIXth Century* (trans. Edwardes), iii, 46 and 76.

beautiful, and enduring. Pepys described it as "a very handsome garment". It has been said that what finally killed it was the action of Louis XIV who clothed his lackeys therein, a significant revenge and one which had the unusual effect of making Charles II look uncommonly foolish. What is certain is that within a few years Paris had regained her dominating position and that the king was obliged to obey her decrees as were his courtiers. In this incident we have no more than an extreme example of the impotence of monarchs when they attempt sumptuary legislation[1] (qvs). It may, however, be said that it is by gentler and more oblique methods that a leader of fashion may compel imitation; thus during the 'seventies and 'eighties of the last century the Princess of Wales was able to exert a considerable influence upon feminine dress. In its details the prevailing mode was certainly affected by her taste. But it would have been quite impossible for her to have reintroduced the crinoline, or even in 1885 to have reverted to the fashions of 1875, for the sufficient reason that these outmoded fashions had become odious to the fashionable world, and of course to her, as to everyone else. Sartorial morality is as potent in its effect upon the leader of fashion as upon the follower, and the canons thereof are determined by no one individual.

It has been said that it is the dressmakers who impose a new fashion upon the public in order to stimulate the market and thus to fill their pockets. The suggestion has a reasonable air for it is after all the great firms and not their customers which design and create the fashions;[2]

[1] An exception is the sumptuary legislation of Kemal Ataturk, by which European dress was introduced into Turkey and the *yashmak* abolished. The history of other Arab states would, however, suggest that Kemal did no more than accelerate a process which is being accomplished elsewhere by voluntary methods.

[2] Even so it is the textile manufacturer whose products are of the first importance in determining the cut of a dress. See Appendix A.

but there are insuperable difficulties in the way of such an explanation. Are we for instance to suppose that tailors have become less avaricious than modistes, do economic laws not function differently for different sexes? Again it must be allowed that the creators of fashion industries do not serve their own interests very well; had they done so there could never have been a vogue for simplicity, and yet it was at a time when the trade was more highly organised than ever before that the very simple style of the 'twenties was at its apogee and skirts at their height; the designers did in fact attempt to bring long skirts for daily wear back to fashion, but they failed.[1] Many other attempts of the same nature, accompanied sometimes by adroit and costly propaganda, have been tried without success. Finally it must be realised that the process of change began at a time when most clothes were actually made in the home and that it has continued through many phases of organisation and mechanisation which, though they have increased the scope and velocity of change, have not altered its nature. In a free market the relationship between the consumer and the producer is in its essence one of unity; the great houses dictate to their *clientèle*, but only because they are certain of acquiescence. It is only because they please that they prosper and if not prosperous they cannot command.

Here is the testimony of M. Paul Poiret, one of the greatest designers and *couturiers* of this century and a man not given to excessive modesty. Speaking to a concourse of ladies in the United States in the late 'twenties he said:

"I know that you think me a king of fashion. It is what your newspapers call me, and it is thus that I am received,

---

[1] See Nystrom, *The Economics of Fashion* (New York, 1928), i, 13-17; iii, 82; xii, 299-300 *et passim*. See also Stuart Chase, *The Tragedy of Waste* (Macmillan, 1925), p. 92.

honoured, and fêted everywhere by great multitudes of people. It is a reception which cannot but flatter and of which I cannot complain. All the same I must undeceive you with regard to the powers of a king of fashion. We are not capricious despots such as wake up one fine day, decide upon a change in habits, abolish a neckline, or puff out a sleeve. We are neither arbiters nor dictators. Rather we are to be thought of as the blindly obedient servants of woman, who for her part is always enamoured of change and athirst for novelty. It is our role, and our duty, to be on the watch for the moment at which she becomes bored with what she is wearing, that we may suggest at the right instant (*à point nommé*) something else which will meet her tastes and needs. It is therefore with a pair of antennae and not with a rod of iron that I come before you, and it is not as a master that I speak, but as a slave, a slave, though, who must divine your innermost thoughts." [1]

In another lecture we find the following profoundly significant anecdote:

"There are signs which allow one to proclaim the end of a fashion. Very few people can recognise them. Thus when I announced that hats would henceforth be plain, it was because I saw them to be smothered with leaves, fruit, flowers, feathers, and ribbons. All fashions end in excess. Nevertheless, on the morrow of that announcement I received a delegation of manufacturers, makers of flowers, fruits, ribbons, and leaves, who, like the burghers of Calais, came to implore me to restore trimmings. But what can one do against the wishes or the desires of women? Hats continued plain, and are so still, and I am heartily sorry for it." [2]

The essential difficulty in the way of any explanation which sees an individual, whether he be a monarch or a tailor, as the prime mover in the history of fashion is, not that these autocrats have frequently been unable to stand against the current of taste, but that we are still

[1] A free translation of *En habillant l'époque*, by Paul Poiret, xviii, p. 266.
[2] *Ibid.* p. 271. The whole of this chapter is of the greatest interest and importance. It should perhaps be said that M. Poiret makes some prophecies which have not been wholly fulfilled.

D

left with no explanation as to why the leaders should desire to make a change or the followers be willing to obey them.

This brings us naturally to the theory of "Human Nature" of which Paul Nystrom is the ablest exponent; he is, incidentally, the only writer on the subject whom I have found to acknowledge the importance of Veblen. Nystrom concludes his examination of human motives with the following summary:

. . . The specific motive or factors for fashion interest and fashion changes, in addition to the physical reasons for change such as occur at the end of each season, are the boredom or fatigue with the current fashion, curiosity, desire to be different or self-assertion, rebellion against convention, companionship and imitation. There may be other factors in human nature promoting fashion interest, but these are sufficiently effective and inclusive upon which to build a practical theory of fashion.[1]

This is no doubt true enough as far as it goes; we have here a sufficient catalogue of human motives, but obviously it leaves a great deal unexplained. Why, for instance, should these human motives have expired among men and yet persisted among women at the beginning of the nineteenth century, and why should they have been absent in China until our own times? We may here have an accurate account of states of mind, but we do not have the reasons which produce them, the motor of fashion itself. We can only conclude that human nature is itself subject to fashion.

In this connection we cannot afford to pass over those theories of dress which relate the outer man to the inner mind. The very important bearing which sexual display and the related phenomena of modesty have upon clothes is discussed in a learned work by Professor J. C. Flugel,[2] who shows very clearly how the erotic imagina-

[1] Nystrom, *op. cit.* p. 87.          [2] Flugel, *op. cit.*

tion plays upon clothes, their putting on, their taking off, the phallic shapes which they assume, both in the conscious and unconscious apprehension of man. It would seem, in the light of his researches, that the sexual differentiation which is so marked a feature of modern dress may well be a centrepiece in our imaginative equipment. But however valuable these investigations into the use to which our conscious and unconscious minds put our clothes and those of our neighbours may be, they do not help us to understand the forces at work which change the form of these symbols. (In fairness to Professor Flugel it must be said that he makes no such claim.) What the psychologists do show, is the enormous importance which attaches to the history of dress. For unless the shape of clothes be a mere peg upon which we hang a sexual imagery, neither changing nor yet changed thereby, we must suppose that the whole relationship between the sexes has undergone a most drastic alteration during the last hundred and fifty years, and that the directives of the unconscious are themselves directed by a stronger power. The sexual impulse may after all, broadly speaking, be regarded as a constant affect upon the course of history, but we are here dealing with something which is by definition a variable. If we are to look for the causes of fashionable change we shall surely find them among those historical forces which are themselves in a perpetual flux, such as can, for instance, explain why men's fashions became stable while those of women continued to evolve, or why the attire of children, for so long similar to that of adults, has obtained a character of its own.

In considering the role of the unconscious a concrete instance may not be amiss. Let us take a favourite of the psychologists, the high-heeled shoe. Flugel explains the actual persistence of this fashion on the ground that it gives an upright carriage, that it effaces the abdomen, that it gives additional height without breadth (*i.e.* a youthful figure), that the size of the foot is thereby diminished and that the heel provides a phallic symbol. [1]

Now before passing to our main objection we may notice that, although all these statements may well be true, within their particular context, the youthful fashion of the Directoire adopted a flat slipper, and that many of the above advantages could have meant but little to Louis XIV.

But the main difficulty is this: the psychologists can explain to us why the high-heeled shoe came into fashion, but they cannot show wherefore it went out again. To say that mankind is fickle and shifts its attention from one member to another is the only answer which the exponent of "Human Nature" can adduce. But it is in truth no answer. China was content with one style of feminine footwear for a thousand years, why must we vary our fetish? Any explanation which is based upon the nature of human nature leaves us, as Plekhanov pointed out a long time ago, just where we started. What we have to discover is the force which makes the Europeans hanker for novelties, while the Chinese remain content with the robes of their ancestors; in other words, we seek for the determinants of human nature itself.

This brings us naturally to the consideration of events outside human nature, such as climate, trade and the intercourse of nations, accidents, wars, revolutions, and the emergence of new moral and political ideas.

Of climate little need be said, it is only under protest that men will change their clothes to suit their climate. It has taken many years to persuade Europeans that a

---

[1] Flugel, *op. cit.* p. 161.

special fashion is needed for life in India. The form of clothes may sometimes originate from climatic needs, but it develops almost in defiance thereof.

Trade and foreign influences, especially foreign conquests, certainly play their part in the development of dress. The effect of conquest can be measured fairly well in the history of China: here for instance the Tartar conquest brought the Tartar cap; in the same way the barbarians who overran the Roman Empire influenced, and were influenced by, the Roman dress. But once such a conquest has been completed the process of change stops. Foreign influences are sometimes hard to distinguish from fashion itself; wherever a more sumptuous style is encountered it tends to be imitated: the history of German fashions, for instance, is almost entirely a history of foreign influences. But if the flow of importation stops, it does not necessarily lead to any further development. This has in fact been demonstrated in the more backward of the Latin American states, where European importations have created static local costumes.

Trade, in the sense of the importation of new materials, does not seem to create new fashions, although it may sometimes affect those already in existence, as in the case of Indian stuffs at the beginning of the eighteenth century; it may be fairly classed as a secondary influence, subordinate to the general trend of fashion and itself deeply affected thereby — witness the ruined ostrich farms of South Africa.

Accidents would seem sometimes to determine details, as, for instance, when the victors of Steinkirk were so hurried in their toilette that they inadvertently set the style for a new cravat, or when Lord Spencer burnt his coat-tails and set a new fashion in jackets. But the continuous and regular development of fashion does not suggest that it owes its direction to a series of accidents, but rather that the accident itself has to be of a kind to meet the trend of the moment, if it is to be of any value in setting a new style.

It is the greater historical movements which find most favour among the theorists as a determinant of fashion; there are indeed many who see an intimate relationship between fashion and politics, in its widest sense. Thus J. M. Price:

> In any investigation of the precepts which have governed feminine fashion, it will be found that, in every country and at all periods of time, the mind of woman has been strongly affected by the ethical atmosphere of her time, and, consciously or unconsciously, has formulated a record of history in her dress.[1]

Once again it must be borne in mind that the theory breaks down if applied to any civilisation but our own. It must also be admitted that in Europe itself such conflicts as the Thirty Years' War and the War of the Spanish Succession produced hardly any perceptible change in the clothes worn by the men and women of the time; that London and Paris have for long been the only capitals of fashion, and that their authority has been respected even by states with which they have been at war; finally, that of the religious and political revolutions which have occurred in these, the capitals of fashion, only two have had a catastrophic influence upon dress; to wit: the Puritan Revolution in England and the French Revolution of 1789.

I think that it is the latter event that has impressed the historians, and, what with that and the difficulty of reconciling all political events with the trends of fashion, the historical theory has been refined to a point at which the historian finds it convenient to invoke the aid of an

---

[1] J. M. Price, *Dame Fashion* (London, 1913).

independent force superior to human volition, an autonomous spiritual entity which governs us unperceived. Mr. Laver, the most recent and most eloquent apologist of this "Time Spirit" or "Zeitgeist", speaks of it thus:

> In every period costume has some essential line, and when we look back over the fashions of the past we can see quite clearly what it is, and can see what is surely very strange, that the forms of dresses, apparently so haphazard, so dependent on the whim of the designer, have an extraordinary relevance to the spirit of the age. The aristocratic stiffness of the old *régime* in France is completely mirrored in the brocaded gowns of the eighteenth century. The republican yet licentious notions of the Directoire find their echo in the plain transparent dresses of the time. Victorian modesty expressed itself in a multitude of petticoats, the emancipation of the post-War flapper in short hair and short skirts. We touch here something very mysterious, as if the Time Spirit were a reality, clothing itself ever in the most suitable garments and rejecting all others. One is almost driven back on the mystical conception of a Zeitgeist who determines for us every detail of our lives, down to gestures, turns of phrases, and even thoughts.[1]

Now, apart from the philosophical difficulties of such a standpoint, it is important to notice that the correspondence between the spirit of the age and the clothes it makes us wear is less complete than might be supposed from the foregoing passage.

The aristocratic stiffness of the old *régime* in France is reflected in British dress of the period without substantial modification; fashion is international. The republican yet licentious notions of the Directoire influenced the dress of Madrid [2] as well as that of Paris; fashion transcends political differences. Victorian London followed in its main lines the fashions of the not

---

[1] James Laver, *Taste and Fashion* (London, 1937), chap. xviii, p. 250.

[2] See Fischel and von Boehn, *op. cit.* i, 155.

so modest court of Napoleon III (as also did Simla and Boston); fashion is outrageous. The short hair and short skirts of the flapper were adopted, not only by the young and emancipated, but by the middle-aged; fashion affects both sexes and all age groups.

In a word, though the fashion would certainly seem to have some relevance to the spirit of the age as manifested in its political and social ideologies, yet it can penetrate where those ideologies cannot. Conversely, the Zeitgeist itself would seem almost powerless to affect the dress of some who may be deeply infected by the spirit of the age. Why do men now resist the Zeitgeist with so much more success than women?

To all these objections it may be replied: that is the way the Zeitgeist works, we are not here dealing with a simple weathercock which turns precisely to all the spiritual winds of humanity, but with a hidden and mysterious force ungoverned by ideological conditions: "Woman is the mould into which the spirit of the age pours itself"; [1] in other words, the force at work is arbitrary and indifferent in its action.

If we allow sufficient premises and permit the Zeitgeist a free hand, there can be no objection. But the argument resolves itself into a tautology: the fashion is what it is because the Zeitgeist makes it so. The theory then becomes, not an explanation based upon facts, but a supernatural hypothesis. If on the other hand we are to attempt to find a rational basis, to correlate the ethical, political, religious, national, or aesthetic ideas in the minds of men with the dress they wear in various ages, we shall encounter insuperable difficulties because fashion so clearly cuts across the ideological barriers.

The supernatural hypothesis has been carried a stage further by Mr. Gerald Heard, a speculator more daring

[1] Laver, *loc cit.*

and far less erudite than Mr. Laver. This theory explains fashion as the product of the "Life Force" or evolutionary appetite, as the work, not of man, but of God. "The thesis of this book is that evolution is going on no longer in but around man, and the faster because working in a less resistant medium." [1]

That such a statement may appear slightly ridiculous has not escaped the author's attention.

. . . The statement that in clothes we are still witnessing creation at work, that in the people's "Sunday Best" alone it is still not resting from its labours, that in a matter held so insignificant the supreme force of the universe is alone visible, that the same dynamo design which once made our bodies for good or ill and now seems to have left them to be maintained at our costs or cut down, is still moving mysteriously though faintly in, of all unlikely things, our garments, the *ignis abyssi* smouldering but alone alight on, of all unlikely altars, the tailor's bench—such a contention may seem to the ordinary well or ill dressed man simply ridiculous. It needs defence, and, not for that reason only, ridicule is usually evidence of misunderstanding. [2]

Nor, it must be confessed, does the argument lack force. There is, as we have noted above, an astonishing similarity between the development of clothes and that of species; there is the same slow development of forms, the same increase in specialisation, the conservation of vestigial members, and, as it may appear after so tedious an examination of rival theories, the same dark mystery. Does not the constant defeat of sumptuary laws suggest a fruitless struggle with a living thing?

The usual difficulties, however, must be advanced; to begin with, there is the example of China. "There," says Mr. Heard, "at once we see we are faced with a people who for some reason are rational, consciously

*Narcissus, an Anatomy of Clothes*, by Gerald Heard (London, 1924), p. 19.
[2] *Ibid.* p. 16.

utilitarian, in a way that we have hardly ever attained."[1] Hence their lack of development (it will be seen that a race theory has had to be invoked). As for the bound foot, that is explained in quite another manner.

The bound foot of the Chinese woman is shaped and shod so as to resemble a hoof, and is a late importation; it may be as late as and associated with the horse hoof sleeve and cuff which conceal the Chinese hand and are said to be a Manchu totemistic fashion, as they, through their irresistible cavalry, mounted the celestial throne from horseback. What more natural, then, that the heightening of sexual charm should be obtained by a distortion with the same tendency? A race memory of immeasureable age was roused by the recollection of late national glory.[2]

Apart from the grave historical objections to such an account, one may reasonably ask what part is played by the long finger-nail of the scholar; this is not exactly a rational adornment, but neither is it the mark of a "horsey" man. But the real trouble about China from the Heardian point of view is that which attaches to any racial view of dress, for how on such a hypothesis are we to account for the abandonment of the traditional dress of China in favour of that of the West? "The Chinese are always strangely interested in finish. They are a people who seem born refined, reflective, recollective."[3] None of which really explains why they have remained indifferent to the urgings of the "Life Force", nor yet why the young Chinese of today turn to Savile Row and the Rue de la Paix for their clothes.

The evolutionary view of dress as presented by Heard is, however, open to more sweeping objections. The process of evolution as we know it in animals is one in which the fittest survive, in which the claims of utility are inexorable. As we have seen, the contrary is true of dress; if we were able to find some animal which

[1] Heard, *op. cit.* p. 71.      [2] *Ibid.* p. 74.      [3] *Ibid.* p. 71.

had evolved in the direction of greater and greater unfitness for existence, until finally it was reduced to a condition in which it had to depend upon the good will of other species for its support, then we should have an exact parallel to the evolutionary process (as regards any given phase of fashion). Certain Japanese poultry do indeed fulfil these conditions, but they are the product of artificial, not of natural, selection.

It may, however, be argued that some animal finery is not, in the strictest sense, utilitarian. The tail of the peacock, the gorgeous rump of the mandril, would appear to be sexual stimulants useful only in courtship. May we not, then, suppose that the brilliant mating colours of animals have been evolved in the same way as the fine dress of humans and for a similar purpose? I think not; when any peacock meets any peahen it would seem to require a certain manifestation of splendour before it can cooperate in the reproductive process. Are we to suppose that a similar necessity exists as between ladies and gentlemen? And if that be the case, must we not believe that a singular frigidity pertains among the higher income groups of the western world? It is indeed an awe-inspiring thought that the frantic distortions and encumbrances in the dress of the wealthy and their liveried servants result from a genteel difficulty in procreation. Happily this does not seem to be the case; although there are certainly economically determined standards of sexual charm, such as small hands and feet, daintiness, and delicacy of complexion, there is abundant evidence that the classes can interbreed freely, and do so without any apparent loss of fertility.

The evolutionary hypothesis breaks down because evolution deals in species, whereas dress is divided neither by races nor by nations, but by classes and groups of classes.

It will have been noticed that in this examination of the theories of fashion we have been obliged to reject one explanation after another because each has failed to tally with the known facts which we set forth at the beginning of this chapter. These facts can be conveniently recited under six headings; they are as follows:

(1) Fashion as we know it in the West is not, and never was universal, it is a product of Europe and is of comparatively recent date.

(2) Fashion is an expanding force, it affects an ever greater number of people in an ever greater part of the world.

(3) Fashion is international and unideological, it springs in the main from two capitals, it is indifferent to the ideological changes outside those capitals.

(4) Of all the convulsions which have taken place in the capitals of fashion only two have had a quite indubitable effect upon the clothes worn by men and women, namely the Puritan Revolution and the French Revolution of 1789.

(5) Fashion has increased sexual differentiation in dress.

(6) Fashion is not quite universal in its influence and permits the survival of certain archaistic forms.

It will at once be apparent that these historical facts constitute an insuperable objection to all theories which start with a generalisation concerning human nature, if that entity is to be considered as something universal and unchanging. They also make it impossible to arrive at a complete correspondence between the history, race, sentiments, ideals, or institutions of a nation and its fashions. Finally they are destructive of any biological explanation. Nor can we allow the movement of fashion to be the result of all or some of the factors here discussed acting in combination; although many of them do, no doubt, play their part in shaping the fashion, the operation of those factors is not confined to Europe; indeed we find them combined in almost any complex civilisation, but the requisite force to set them into motion, to put them to account, and, having once started the engine, to accelerate it to an ever-increasing degree, is lacking. The nature of this force is to be sought along other lines, lines which have been indicated by Veblen. It is by the application of his theories that we can meet the objections here proposed and thus come at a theory which will, at least, tally with the salient facts in the history of clothes.

# CHAPTER FOUR

## MUTATION

> Does not the world love *Court Guides*, and millinery, and plate
> and carriages? Mercy on us! Read the fashionable intelligence, read
> the *Court Circular*; read the genteel novels, survey mankind from
> Pimlico to Red Lion Square, and see how the Poor Snob is aping
> the Rich Snob; how the Mean Snob is grovelling at the feet of the
> Proud Snob; and the Great Snob is lording it over his humble
> brother. Does the idea of equality ever enter Dives' head? Will it
> ever? Will the Duchess of Fitzbattleaxe (I like a good name) ever
> believe that Lady Croesus, her next-door neighbour in Belgrave
> Square, is as good a lady as her Grace? Will Lady Croesus ever
> leave off pining for the Duchess's parties, and cease patronising
> Mrs. Broadcloth, whose husband has not got his Baronetcy yet?
> Will Mrs. Broadcloth ever heartily shake hands with Mrs. Seedy,
> and give up those odious calculations about poor dear Mrs. Seedy's
> income? Will Mrs. Seedy, who is starving in her great house, go and
> live comfortably in a little one, or in lodgings? Will her landlady,
> Miss Letsam, ever stop wondering at the familiarity of the trades-
> people, or rebuking the insolence of Suky, the maid, who wears
> flowers under her bonnet like a lady?
>
> W. M. THACKERAY, *The Book of Snobs*, xxxvi

THE easiest manner of approaching our problem will,
I think, be to look at the manner in which one
particular garment has undergone mutation. Thereby
we shall be able to see, in an admittedly diagrammatic
way, how and why the mechanism works.

Somewhere about the middle of the nineteenth century
the Duchess of Fitzbattleaxe was pleased to extend the
already large area covered by her skirts by means of a
light metal contrivance called a crinoline. The crinoline enabled her to increase her volume without adding to
her weight, it made possible an extension which, under
normal circumstances, would have been virtually impossible. For the crinoline came opportunely at the end of

a long process of aggrandisement, which may be said to
have started (we can draw no line) in the 'twenties and
'thirties of the century. For many years skirts were
expanded by the addition of more and more petticoats,
then in the 'forties pneumatic hoops made their appearance, but even these could not sustain the dimensions of
the true crinoline, which, at its greatest width, filled
rooms, blocked doorways, and overflowed from carriages. To have walked in one of these in a high wind
must have been a considerable feat of navigation. It
will be seen that the thing was undoubtedly an instrument of conspicuous leisure.

The example of the duchess was, of course, sufficient
for Lady Croesus; clearly the crinoline was "being
worn", so she wore one; then, of course, Mrs. Broadcloth
must have one too, and if Mrs. Broadcloth why not Mrs.
Seedy and Miss Letsam, until finally Suky the maid,
also has one, just as she has flowers under her bonnet
(see Plate 4).

By the time that the crinoline has made its way into
the servants' hall, with results depicted by Leech, it has
in the strictest sense of the word become vulgar.[1] What
then is the duchess to do? It is unthinkable that she
should be seen wearing the same costume as that of
Lady Croesus, not to speak of Mrs. Seedy and Miss
Letsam. The obvious reply is to forbid her emulative
neighbour to wear any such thing. This in effect is what
her ancestors did do; if we look at the sumptuary laws
of the Middle Ages we shall find again and again that
their overt purpose is to ensure a proper degree of class
distinction in dress.[2] But, as we have seen, these laws
were disregarded; the Croesus family seems to have been

---

[1] Crinolines were actually worn by girls working in the fields in East Prussia in
1865: see Fischel and Boehn, iii, 58.
[2] See von Boehn, i, 251 *et passim*.

PLATE 4

**CAUSE AND EFFECT.**

*Housemaid.* "Drat the bothering China cups and things. They be always a-knocking up against one's Crinoline."

Vulgarisation of the Crinoline
*From ' Punch ', March 26, 1864*

too resolute, and in time the legal struggle was
abandoned. Moreover it is possible that the Battleaxes
were not averse to being imitated by the Croesuses so
long as they were not overtaken. The essential thing
was that the nobility should maintain its lead. What
then could be attempted? The obvious thing was to
increase the size of the crinoline; this had two advantages;
in the first place it altered the fashion so that the duchess
again became its leader, in the second place it made the
crinoline still more unpractical and therefore more
difficult to imitate. But of course this move led only to
a repetition of the emulative process, the circumference
of the duchess expands until we get the situation pictured
in Plate 5.

The process did not of course proceed in jumps, there
was always a restraining influence to prevent the
vulgarity of eccentricity and there were also other ways
in which the fashion could be altered, changes of colour
and material, in hats, in sleeves, and in the dressing of
hair. It will moreover be found that as an aristocrat
the duchess did not hesitate to outbid her rival in a
generous display of shoulders and bosom. Here indeed
Mrs. Broadcloth, whose husband, perhaps, was a
dissenter, may have been frightened out of the game,
but Lady Croesus would not have hesitated to try a
show-down with the duchess. This device of conspicuous outrage worked with more effect in the seventeenth century than in the nineteenth, and is, because of
its narrower scope, pushed to less extreme limits in any
one direction, but, as we have already noticed, in the
history of feminine dress the focus of attention shifts
continually from one part of the person to another and
there is in consequence always some new manner in
which dress can be shockingly immodest and therefore
fashionable.

PLATE 5

**THE SAFEST WAY OF TAKING A LADY DOWN TO DINNER.**

Hypertrophy of the Crinoline
*From ' Punch ', October 1st, 1864*

Now it is to be noticed that throughout the entire process of development disapproving voices are raised, jokes are cracked, sermons preached, the medical profession invoked, etc. It is by no means certain that these criticisms are a deterrent to the fashionable, and that they are not rather in the nature of encouragements. For, as we have seen, the leaders of fashion are attempting to escape, as much as to compel, imitation. To those who feel strong enough to leap them the barriers erected by the Church and the press are welcome; moreover it is the imitators rather than the innovators who incur the chief censure, it is as though the hurdles were set higher after the leaders in the race have cleared them.

Nevertheless on this occasion the protests came from a quarter which, supposing the pre-eminence of the individual, might well be thought authoritative. Not only did Queen Victoria abjure the crinoline, but, what was much more important, the Empress of the French, with whom it is always associated, did likewise. Both attempts failed, the thing persisted, despite the efforts of both sovereigns, until about 1866,[1] when, after a continual development of about twenty years, the duchess was, so to speak, pushed to her extremities. Mere enlargement being rendered impossible as a result of those limiting factors to which we referred in Chapter Two, the crinoline declined. But its end like its beginning was slow, first the skirt was looped up in front to show an elaborate underskirt, it then tailed away into a long train which was eventually gathered up into a bustle, and therewith a new mode was born. At every stage of its development it maintained the characteristics of sumptuous dress. At each point the duchess was more fashionable, more ladylike, than her competitors, at each stage the emulative process was at work.

[1] Nystrom, p. 279. Fischel and von Boehn, v, 76.

In its broad essentials such a view of the mechanism
of change is very far from being new or revolutionary.
Mr. Laver adopts it,[1] as also does Hazlitt, who has
described the emulative process in terms which cannot
be bettered.

Fashion is an odd jumble of contradictions, of sympathies
and antipathies. It exists only by its being participated among
a number of persons, and its essence is destroyed by being
communicated to a greater number. It is a continual struggle
between "the great vulgar and the small" to get the start of,
or keep up with each other in the race of appearances, by an
adoption on the part of the one of such external and fantastic
symbols as strike the attention and excite the envy or admiration
of the beholder, and which are no sooner made known and
exposed to public view for this purpose, than they are successfully copied by the multitude, the slavish herd of imitators,
who do not wish to be behindhand with their betters in outward
show and pretensions, and then sink without any further notice
into disrepute and contempt. Thus fashion lives only in a
perpetual round of giddy imitation and restless vanity. To be
old fashioned is the greatest crime a coat or a hat can be guilty
of. To look like nobody else is a sufficiently mortifying reflection; to be in danger of being mistaken for one of the rabble is
worse. Fashion constantly begins and ends in the two things
it abhors most, singularity and vulgarity.[2]

This is admirable, but perhaps the essayist may be
thought a little too severe when he goes on to say that

[fashion] . . . is not anything in itself, nor a sign of anything
but the folly and vanity of those who rely upon it as their
greatest pride and ornament . . . fashion is the abortive issue
of vain ostentation and exclusive egotism: it is haughty, affected,
trifling, servile, despotic, mean and ambitious, precise and
fantastical all in a breath—tied to no rule and bound to
conform to every whim of the minute.[3]

[1] Laver, *op. cit.* p. 254-6. But here the social element is seen only as causing
fashions to go out. It is difficult to see the going out and coming in of a fashion
otherwise than as the opposing aspects of one process.
[2] Hazlitt, *Sketches and Essays, On Fashion.*
[3] *Ibid.*

Hazlitt over-simplifies the motives of those who follow the fashion, and that today is all of us, as I also have over-simplified in the account of mutation given above. I have of course stated the process of competitive emulation in too plain a way. It is an account of actions rather than of motives, of classes rather than of individuals. Such a degree of ratiocination and so conscious a pursuit of competitive advantage are not present in the mind of the duchess when she chooses a dress or in that of the housemaid when she buys a reach-me-down. No snob ever describes his own particular form of emulation as snobbery. Nor am I supposing that those manifold emotions of the snob, the desire to be decent, to be "in the swim", as good as the next man, smart, up to date, respectable, etc., are paramount considerations in the mind of the consumer. Beauty, in its purest sense, sexual advertisement, modesty, utility even, may be of the first consideration when the purchase is made. Nevertheless there is a constant determinant, to some extent imposed by the producer, to some extent immanent in the sartorial morality of the consumer, which guides his or her choice inexorably in the fashionable direction. I believe that this truth is capable of experimental verification. If two retailers were to compete at the same prices I think that he who neglected the fashion would not only lose custom, but would find his wares adjudged less pretty, less becoming, and even, when he had lagged too far behind, less modest and less practical than those of his rival, for at a certain point in their development we are unable to find any quality in the creations of the past but a grotesque dowdiness and a dreary indecency (that particular mode of fashionable outrage having ceased to be customary).

It would seem, in short, that the emulative process is so strong that it distorts even our sense of what is sexually charming and intrinsically beautiful. This truth may easily be established by a glance at Plates 13, 14, or 15. However could we have felt such enthusiasm for such frightful clothes? It is true that some women may complain that the fashion is unfavourable to their age or particular type of beauty, they may even contrive minor adjustments in their dress in order to rectify this injustice, but they can never break altogether with the prevailing mode. Consider how many lovely necks must have been hidden by a ruff between 1570 and 1620, what legs have gone unseen to the grave.

If we allow the mainspring of fashion to be the emulative process whereby the members of one class imitate those of another, who in their turn are driven to ever new expedients of fashionable change, then, I think, we shall find that the first three of the objections raised in our last chapter can be resolved without difficulty.

*Objection No. 1 : Fashion a European Phenomenon.*—Clearly if our account be true, fashionable change can occur only when wealth is so distributed in a society as to allow more than one class to afford the luxury of sumptuous dress. There must, in addition to the ruling class, be a middle class, and this middle class must have the power, financial and political, to vie with that above it, to imitate its dress and to defy its sumptuary laws. Such a class must be constantly increasing in power and in wealth in relation to the highest class; otherwise a point must soon be reached at which it is distanced in the race, obliged to fall into a secondary rank and forgo emulation. In other words the society which produces changing fashions must itself be a society which is changing. Surely we have here the obvious difference between the civilisation of Europe and that of China.

It may be that fashion owes its origin in Europe to the

importation of sumptuous foreign clothes from Byzantium, and later, with the Crusades, from the Levant. This would appear to be the view of Herr von Boehn, but in discussing the changes which supervened at the beginning of the fourteenth century he says:

The chief change was the apparent loss of a standard of what had so far passed for propriety. In the arrogance of its newly acquired wealth the rising middle class recognised no bounds, it must and would enjoy life. It did not desire to emulate the knights, but to outshine them. This aim naturally manifested itself most obviously in dress, for dress is the agency through which any new consciousness of the world and one's particular *milieu* is most speedily proclaimed. Not only did new modes arise, but they changed with far greater frequency than before; fashion, in the sense of incessant fluctuation, perpetual striving after improvement, now came on the scene.[1]

*Objection No. 2: Fashion an Expanding Force.*—As the middle class has risen to power and established itself as the ruling class in Europe it has called into existence a great urban proletariat, and at the same time it has created machinery whereby any given fashion can be speedily and cheaply imitated. Thus the conflict is perpetuated. The middle class, which is, of course, by no means without its hierarchy, must look to the competition of the labouring classes, which, as we shall discover, are assisted by some later developments of fashion.

*Objection No. 3: Fashion is International and Unideological.*—The basis of sartorial morality is a set of pecuniary values, values which are obviously of very wide application. The traditional dress of China and the fashionable dress of Europe may stand as opposite poles in the consideration of fashionable change, but they are at one in their insistence upon conspicuous

[1] Von Boehn, i, 215.

leisure. It is not therefore unnatural that a foreign mode, where it can claim superior sumptuosity, should be preferred even where national prejudices are affronted.

For instance, the national dress of the Irish, the knee breeches, pudding-shaped hat, and cut-away jacket of the man, and the short skirts and shawl of the woman, were a reality at the beginning of the nineteenth century and something distinctively national and un-English. Throughout the century and indeed up to our own day the spirit of Irish nationalism has grown despite all that the sister island could do in the way of conciliation and coercion. As a result efforts have been made, not only to secure political autonomy, but to preserve and cultivate the national language, and this despite manifest inconveniences and difficulties. Simultaneous with this movement there has been a complete abandonment of the national dress, so that today a photograph of a crowd in Dublin is indistinguishable from that of one in London or Oslo. This seeming paradox has been repeated in every European State where the spirit of nationalism has been aroused. Sartorial morality, the desire to appear to belong to an upper class, is stronger than patriotism.

What *is* shown in the costume of a people is the extent to which it has been affected by the modern industrial system. Fashion affects a country, not in accordance with its religion, its polity, or its national aspirations, but in accordance with its degree of commercial development. Thus states as different as Russia, Spain, Greece, and Persia retained their national costumes in the face of mass-produced fashions much more successfully than such highly developed countries as Germany, Belgium, Denmark, and Japan, while England, the home of modern industrial development, was the first to lose her peasant dress. It is moreover to be remarked in this connection that where national costumes have survived in a partially industrialised state, they have done so largely by becoming a festival attire and in their most sumptuous form.

An understanding of the emulative process and of its implications makes it clear enough, I think, why change in fashion depends upon a changing society, why the scope of fashion is determined by the degree of industrial development, and why fashion can leap all barriers between one state and another given some similarity in the class structure of the countries concerned. But our other objections remain. For, on the face of it, there is no reason why the process of fashionable change should not consist in a mutation of sumptuous styles without any correspondence to ideological changes; but we have admitted that in at least two instances such changes have occurred. The examination thereof deserves a chapter to itself.

# CHAPTER FIVE

# REVOLUTION

> There is to be a ball at Windsor on Friday for the Prince's birthday, which has not lately been noticed there. Lord Lorn and seven other young men of fashion were invited to it. It seems they now crop their hair short and wear no powder, which not being the etiquette yet, the youths, instead of representing that they are not fit to appear so docked, sent excuses that they were going out of town, or were unavoidably engaged—a message one would think dictated by old Prynne or Tom Paine, and certainly unparalleled in all the books in the Lord Chamberlain's office.
>
> HORACE WALPOLE to Miss Mary Berry, August 8th, 1791

*OBJECTION No. 4: The Revolutions of 1642 and 1789.*—It will be generally allowed that the revolutions of 1642 and 1789 were not without their effect upon the dress of the men and women of the time and that this fact accords well enough with the view that whatever the actual cause of mutation, the forms to which it gives birth do have a direct relevance to the ideas within men's minds. But in the domain of the spirit Europe has witnessed a revolution no less remarkable than these, and, as one might imagine, of even greater relevance to the decoration of the person. For, when the entire republic of Christendom was shattered by the Reformation the convulsion in belief was accompanied by a change no less great in thought and in the domain of the fine arts. The effect of this catastrophe upon the style of secular dress was so faint as to be hardly perceptible. Divided in religion Europe remained united in dress. The rival parties in France and Germany wore the same clothes, protestant England aped the fashions of her catholic adversary Spain. If there is a schism at this period, it is between Spanish and Italian styles, not between Protestant and Catholic. Nor did the classical revival of the Italian renaissance exercise an influence at all comparable to that of the age of David and Winckelmann.

The only new tendency suggestive of an ideological influence is the increasing use of dark materials. In the Middle Ages both sexes had walked in the most brilliant colours and had carried as much jewelry as possible. The tinctures of dress were similar to those of the escutcheon, with dazzling arrangements of *mi parti*, to enliven the effect; when, in the early 16th century the German peasants revolted, one of their demands was that they might be permitted to wear scarlet like the gentry. The use of black began in the Burgundian Court and is recorded as early as 1468, so that in its origins it can hardly be connected with the reformation or counter-reformation. But such a connection may perhaps be traced in the adoption of this fashion by the Spanish successors of the Burgundians and certainly the popularity of black among the Dutch calvinists, who got the style from the Spanish, may be connected with a religious motive.

It is probable that the English puritans were influenced by their Dutch brethren in this matter, they adopted dark, or at least drab, clothing as a political badge before and during the civil war. That war is unique in being the only one in which non-combatants of the same nation have adopted opposing styles of dress. The Commonwealth men did not actually devise a fashion of their own, though I think they looked to the low countries, while their opponents looked to France, but on the whole their protest was against sumptuosity itself, against the very principle of emulation.

Certainly there was a religious motive in this deliberate dowdiness, but it was a manifestation of religious belief which had been absent in the wars of the League, where the Protestant cause was dominated by an aristocratic faction; it is also just what, given the above explanation of fashionable change, we should expect from a middle class facing a resurgent aristocracy. We shall indeed find that something of the same sort occurred in the early stages of the French Revolution.

After the parliamentarian victory, the emulative process soon came into operation once more; the new ruling class, which was of course far from homogeneous, having ceased to be in opposition, departed slowly, but surely, from its sartorial principles, and long before the Restoration French fashions had begun to creep in.[1] It should also be borne in mind that for all its simplicity the puritan dress was never quite without sumptuosity; it was always the dress of the white-collar worker. The roundhead manifests the "lower", the cavalier the "higher" sumptuosity.

Here, in passing, we may notice what seems to be a marked tendency of the bourgeoisie in modern Europe and a characteristic of its own form of sumptuosity, namely personal cleanliness. Not that a certain nicety of person has not always been well thought of, especially among the Islamic peoples. But in Holland, in England, in the Scandinavian countries, and in the United States soap and water have marched hand in hand with protestantism, commerce, expansion, industry, and a sober but spotless attire. Whether it be that the result of tireless scrubbing is pleasing to those who set industry high among the virtues, while dirt is considered shiftless, feckless, unprincipled, and insolvent, I do not pretend to say. But there would certainly seem to be some affinity between the bourgeoisie and the bath. Among the

---

[1] See London Museum Catalogue, No. 5 (Costume), and the introduction thereto.

catholic peoples on the other hand and wherever a more
or less feudal society persists, stinks are not only in
evidence, but of small account, and dirt a frequent
concomitant of sumptuosity.[1]

The subject of smells brings us naturally to that of
Versailles. It was to Versailles that Restoration England
turned for its fashions after the utter and, as it seemed,
final defeat of the puritan mode. The only difference
between the feminine mode of France and that of
England was that in the latter the element of conspicuous
outrage was exaggerated, and for this it is easy to find
a direct political motive. For men Versailles ruled
supreme, and, as we have seen, could not be dethroned.

Even before Louis XIV attained his majority France
had displaced Spain as the lawgiver of fashion. Holland
soon came into line, as did Italy and Germany; by the
end of the century only Spain and a few of her depend-
encies remained to challenge French taste.

The seal was set upon this victory by the creation of
the palace of Versailles. Never before had Europe seen
so magnificent a setting for conspicuous leisure; the
palace itself carried no vulgar taint of convenience in
administration, nor was the site of any particular beauty;
better still, the ground itself was unsuitable for building,
and many workmen lost their lives in its construction.
The water for the fountains could only be conveyed at
great expense, the building was well away from any
vulgar habitation, and the mere act of getting there
supposed a certain expenditure. Saint Simon, who was
there for so many years, speaks feelingly of the discomforts, the cold and the glaring heat. But then Versailles
was built not for ease, but for Glory.[2]

The same may be said of the courtiers who dwelt

---

[1] But see Havelock Ellis, *Studies in the Psychology of Sex*, I, iv.
[2] *Memoirs*, Ed. Cheruel, XII, iv.

therein. In the beginning, when the king and his mistresses were younger and Versailles was only beginning to arise from its foundations of bog and sand, there was, no doubt, much to please in the life of the court; but that was far from being the case during the long, tedious, and disastrous reign of Mme de Maintenon. The life of the king and of his courtiers was then devoted to a succession of solemn fatuities. Reading the accounts one is astonished at the amount of time wasted by so many talented people, to whom no professions were open save those of arms, the Church, and occasionally diplomacy or administration (but these latter were commonly entrusted to members of the middle class). Take the career of Saint Simon himself; he left the army at the age of 27, because men of lesser birth were promoted before him; explaining his action to Louis, he said that he wished to be nearer His Majesty the better to court him.[1] This courtship consisted in hanging about Versailles, quarrelling, intriguing for ceremonial advantages, and running into debt. Never, until the king's death, did he obtain any kind of real power, and even during the regency his greatest achievements were in matters of precedence. He was a man of outstanding gifts, but unless his memoirs had been published we should never have heard of him.

This honourably futile existence was of course accompanied by enormous expenditure both personal and national. It would almost seem that the canons of pecuniary taste influenced Louis in his conduct of war; the king was never fond of pitched battles, which, however glorious, were bound to involve much toil and confusion. The campaigns, in which he appeared in person with the ladies, centred upon the capture of some strong place; M. le Prince or Turenne could be trusted to amuse the opposing army while the engineers ran

[1] *Memoirs*, Ed. Cheruel, III, xii, 226.

PLATE 6

Examples of futility in French and Spanish dress of the 17th century

parallels to the enemy walls, and battered a breach. Then the king, very much the centre of the picture, watched the defenders march out in brave array and received the compliment of the hostile commander. The entire ceremony was expensive, decorous, glorious, and, so far as the monarch was concerned, not so very dangerous. It was the rarest thing for the defenders to fight in such deadly earnest that they would hold the breaches and expose the city to the danger of a sack.

This kind of thing went on for many years until France was exhausted. When peace was made and there was a breathing space, Louis found it necessary to hold manœuvres so lavish and so grandiose that the expense was greater than that of an actual campaign in the field.

Saint Simon says of Louis that he loved splendour, magnificence, and profusion in everything. Intentionally he made this a matter of principle and inspired his court therewith. He liked to see indulgence in entertainments, in equipage, in building, and in gambling; he put a premium on luxury, for at bottom he liked to see everyone being ruined.[1] Saint Simon saw in this a calculated policy aimed at the reduction of the nobility, and most historians agree with him. But it must be said that the nobles needed but little encouragement in the matter. The easier and more self-indulgent life of Paris or their estates was open to them, but they clung desperately to Versailles; nothing could console them for banishment from a place which they well knew to be both tedious and ruinous and they spent further thousands upon questions of precedence without any encouragement from the monarch.

In the end the king wearied of his own grandeurs; he decided to make himself a little place in the country

[1] *Ibid.* XII, iv, 78.

where he could be quiet with his widow lady. He left Versailles for a discreet valley shut off from the world; there from Wednesday to Saturday at rare intervals he might find solace from the intolerable tedium of the court which he had created. So he went to Marly.

But the machine was too strong for its architect; bit by bit Marly too had to be enlarged, forested, and furnished with those waterworks for which in the end it became celebrated. Marly became the inner paradise of courtiers, grander, because more select, than Versailles and as big a bore.[1]

I have dwelt at some length upon the court of Louis XIV because it is not only the home of a multitude of fashions, but provides also one of the finest illustrations to the Theory of the Leisure Class, especially during those years when its creator was alive. Here we have the life of unproductive labour in its purest form, carried on with a disregard for the comfort of those who led it and of those who were exploited in order that it might be— which leaves one wondering how anyone could have tolerated it for so long. For despite a moment of relaxation under a regent too pleasure loving for the higher futility, the life of Versailles continued until 1789. Versailles was the cynosure and admiration of Europe throughout the eighteenth century. Attempts were made to reproduce it in Caserta, Potsdam, Schönbrunn, and Tsarskoye Selo. Only in this country was its influence resisted with success.

The masculine fashion of Versailles at the height of its glory was a fine example of conspicuous leisure tempered by martial futility. The enormous peruke, heavily cuffed and embroidered coat, ruffled breeches, and high-heeled shoes were just not too unsuitable for the more genteel kind of military operation.

[1] *Memoirs*, Ed. Cheruel, XI, iv, 83.

But the tendency of the eighteenth century is one of slow but steady simplification; the bulky breeches dwindle into small clothes, the sleeves are diminished and both coats reduced, the inner one to a waistcoat, the shoes flattened, plainer and darker colours replace brocade. In nothing is the change more visible than in the wig. (The head is always the most sensitive index of fashionable change.) Wigs which were so vast in the late seventeenth century, decline with only one short revival, until they are reduced to the vestigial tie wig of the late eighteenth century and finally disappear altogether. This decline and fall is portentous; ever since the days of Elisha men have been deeply sensitive to the crowning injustice of nature; the wig gave them a century and a half of immunity. Dignified, not too unpractical in its later stages, above all discreet, it was one of the most flattering contrivances ever invented, and yet it went. By the middle of the nineteenth century even the Established Church had given it up; such is the steady tidal influence of fashion.

In addition to this growth of simplicity we may notice two other eighteenth‑century innovations in masculine dress. First, an increasing tendency to make a sharp distinction between the dress of business and that of ceremony; a change which was in part compensated by the increasing use of ceremonial dress, which became "evening dress". Secondly, the divorce between army uniform and civilian dress.

It will be noticed that these innovations were very much to the advantage of the middle classes; the fashion permitted an occasional sumptuosity on the part of those who led a more or less industrious life. More important still, it placed the civilian upon a footing of equality with the army officer.

The resultant costume was, however, based upon a

notion of Conspicuous Waste, for it was in its essentials
the dress of a country gentleman. It demonstrated a
life largely, though not wholly, futile, devoted to the
honourable pastimes of the countryside. The sword
goes out of fashion, but it is replaced by the riding-crop
of the fox-hunter, from whose attire modern evening
dress is still recognisably descended. The sportsman
has become the ideal type in place of the soldier.

Now, at first sight, this triumph of a middle-class
fashion would seem to contradict all that has been said
concerning the mutation of forms. Here we have the
bourgeois refusing to imitate his betters and imposing a
style of his own. But emulation depends obviously
upon a complete acceptance of the social hierarchy, and
this was precisely what was vanishing throughout the
eighteenth century. Or rather, to put the matter more
exactly, the sartorial standards of England, a country in
which the class structure of the *ancien régime* had never
existed in its entirety, were slowly adopted by France,
where that *régime* was gradually drifting to disaster.
Here indeed we can find a pretty close correspondence
between the ideological and sartorial influences of the
age. The Anglomania which culminated, in the years
immediately preceding the Revolution, in the most
grotesque parody of English habits, was echoed at every
point in the dress of Frenchmen.

There is, however, a further difficulty; in feminine
fashions the emulative process remained almost normal.
Women's dresses remain aristocratic, in the sense of
demonstrating conspicuous leisure, all through the
century and right up to the year 1914 or thereabouts,
with only one violent though short-lived fluctuation at
the time of the French Revolution. The coiffure again
marks its development. At the beginning of the century
the high head-dress named after Mlle de Fontanges

(against which Louis XIV fought in vain for twenty years) gave way to a mode of relative simplicity which was compensated by an increased volume of skirts; throughout the century the hair (or wig) grew again until by the 'eighties it had reached a wild degree of size and fantasy, as had the entire structure of a lady's dress (see Plate 1). It is as though the men were sacrificing their hair, and indeed all their finery, for the benefit of the opposite sex.

We must postpone the explanation of this remarkable phenomenon to our next chapter; here it will be more convenient to examine that momentary deviation from the general line of development which for a time caused the dress of women to follow the same course as that of men.

There was a pre-revolutionary moment when the ladies of Paris succumbed to Anglomania. Fashions of greater simplicity, with a certain out-door influence, the precursors of the modern tailor-made, came into fashion and with them natural hair reappeared. With the Revolution itself, that is to say in its terrific moment, fashion came almost to a full stop. For a time the exhibition of sumptuosity was checked and with it emulation. It is with the Directoire that the revolution in clothes begins again. At that moment the situation was one in which the possibility of emulation had returned, but the old social hierarchy had vanished, the fashion was for a time headless. The result was an astonishing anarchy of styles.[1] Eventually a style was born which met the demands of sumptuosity (largely through conspicuous outrage) while maintaining a revolutionary form.[2]

[1] See Madelin, *La Revolution*, xxxvi and xliv, also *La France de l'Empire*, by the same author, chap. v.

[2] Neither the dress of the *"Incroyable"* nor that of the *"Merveilleuse"* was universally worn. See Ruppert, IV, 54.

The concessions to revolutionary sentiment were indeed of a pretty far-reaching nature. One has only to compare the dress of 1800 (Plate 7) with that of 1776 (Plate 1) to see to what an extent conspicuous leisure, and even conspicuous consumption, had been abandoned.[1] By its rejection of artifice the dress of those times seems to assert the equality of women; it is, in consequence, very unkind to age and to corpulence. Nevertheless, the fashion swept over Europe even more rapidly than did the armies of France. Nor was this style ever replaced by an aristocratic mode, as was the Puritan fashion. Dress was almost unaffected by the Restoration; it continues an unbroken development into the nineteenth century.[2] And in this perhaps it reflects the balance of social forces more accurately than do the successive political constitutions of the age.

The two undoubted exceptions to our remarks concerning the unideological nature of fashion seem to me not to conflict with, but to support, the theory of emulation. On each occasion the change has been towards a kind of simplicity, very different kinds to be sure, but similar in their rejection of the claims of sumptuosity. On each occasion there was a sudden sharpening of the class conflict, with its inevitable repercussion upon the emulative process. If that process is dependent upon the aspirations and development of a resurgent middle class, then it is only natural that a conflict such as that which occurred in 1642 or 1789 should exercise a much more potent influence upon dress than the numerous wars, *coups d'états*, religious convulsions, aesthetic movements, and dynastic changes in which the resurgent middle class has played a subordinate or negligible part.

[1] It should however, be borne in mind that the dress in Plate 1 is for grander occasions than that in Plate 7.

[2] See Ruppert, *Histoire du Costume de l'Antiquité au XIX<sup>e</sup> Siècle*, V, p. 27.

PLATE 7

*Morning Dress for July, 1800.*

In our next chapter we shall attempt to show that the converse is true, and that a silent industrial revolution unmarked by any supreme political convulsion has effected a transformation in dress far greater than that of the French or Puritan Revolutions.

# CHAPTER SIX

# VICARIOUS CONSUMPTION
# —ARCHAISM

"Rot ye, ye great lumberin' beggar!" exclaimed Mr. Jorrocks, furiously indignant; " Rot ye, do ye think I'm like Miss Biffin, the unfortunate lady without harms or legs, that I can't 'elp myself?" continued he, dashing the wet out of his spoon cuff. " Now that's the wust o' your flunkey fellers," continued he in a milder tone to Mrs. Muleygrubs, as the laughter the exclamation caused had subsided. "That's the wust o' your flunkey fellers," repeated he, mopping his arm, "they know they'd never be fools enough to keep fellers to do nothing, and so they must be constantly meddlin'. Now, your women waiters are quite different," continued he: "they only try for the useful, and not for the helegant. There's no flash 'bout them. If they see a thing's under your nose, they let you reach it, and don't bring a dish that's steady on the table round at your back to tremble on their 'ands under your nose. Besides," added our Master, " you never see a bosky Batsay waiter, which is more than can be said of all dog un's."

"But you surely couldn't expect ladies to be waited upon by women, Mr. Jorrocks," exclaimed his astonished hostess.

R. S. SURTEES, *Handley Cross, or Mr. Jorrocks' Hunt*, xxxiv

$O$*BJECTION No. 5: Fashion has Increased Sexual Differentiation in Dress.*—Like all Veblen's ideas, that of Vicarious Consumption seems obvious when stated, but its far-reaching implications are frequently overlooked.

It is a commonplace that we are hardly less sensitive to a lapse of sartorial morality in someone "belonging" to us than in our own persons. The father of a family may complain bitterly of the sums which he is expected to disburse for the apparel of his household, but he will be the first to complain of any shabbiness or impropriety of dress on the part of his wife, his children, his men-servants, his maid-servants, or anything that is his.  Generally speaking, his concern will be much greater where the person affected is bound to him by a tie of economic dependence.  The clothes of parents, business associates, brothers, or colleagues are, comparatively speaking, a matter of indifference; but those of wives, or children unable to earn their own living, or of domestic servants, affect him more nearly perhaps than those which he wears himself.  The display of sumptuosity through the agency of a third person is, of course, nothing new.  At a very early moment in history people of wealth found that their own backs were not broad enough to bear the weight of all the sumptuous dress that they would have liked to display.  The priest or chieftain, not content with dressing finely himself, employed servants, or persons in a servile position, to dress for him; these vicarious consumers, wives, eunuchs, retainers, etc., were at first employed in productive or military tasks.  But here too the law of conspicuous waste came into effect.  It is patently more futile to put a servant into a fine dress and bid him do nothing, and the same, of course, applies to a wife.  Thus we find that notable magnates supported a number of wives out of all proportion to the demands of concupiscence; these ladies served to glorify their owner simply by their number. In the same way it became usual to employ servants whose duties were purely nominal and whose only role was vicarious consumption.  In some cases the futility of these occupations had an ennobling effect.  Thus we find such survivals as the bridesmaids and best man at weddings, and the grooms, equerries, almoners, ladies of the bed-chamber, etc., theoretical servants whose duties, when they have not been changed out of all recognition by later developments in the art of government, consist almost entirely in the wearing of sumptuous dress, and who would be ill thought of were they to perform the manual labour originally entrusted to them.

The great innovation of modern dress was the efface-
ment of the central figure, who had hitherto been the
most gorgeous of the family. This change is the result
of the emergence of a new ruling class. The nobleman,
like the lady, was a creature incapable of useful work;
war and sport were the only outlets for his energy and a
high degree of conspicuous leisure was incumbent upon
him. Equally, it was important that he should in his
own person be a consumer; if he had relied simply upon
the vicarious consumption of his household, it would
have appeared that he was working to support them.
He had to establish the fact that he was a *rentier* (which
until the eighteenth century almost implied the owner-
ship of land).

In the society which emerged with the industrial
revolution idleness was no longer the usual sign of
wealth. The man who worked was not infrequently in
receipt of a larger income than he who drew rents; an
industrious life no longer implied a poor or laborious
existence and ceased therefore to be dishonourable. It
was sufficient, therefore, that a man should demonstrate
by means of his black coat, cylindrical hat, spotless linen,
carefully rolled umbrella, and general air of refined discomfort that he was not actually engaged in the production of goods, but only in some more genteel employment concerned with their division. Masculine dress
betokened a complete abstention from industrial labour,
but that was all; it was not "highly sumptuous".

This masculine escape from the task of displaying the
higher sumptuosity naturally mitigated to a great extent
the necessity for emulation, or rather it made the process
vicarious instead of being direct. The masculine attire
which established itself with the industrial system
changed very little; we may almost say that it is with us

today. Here then was the long-delayed triumph of the drab Puritan over the gaudy Cavalier. The aristocratic style was abolished and a completely civilian mode, a kind of melanic, urbanised version of the eighteenth-century country gentleman's attire, established in its place. Nor is it only the brocade of the nobleman which has gone, but also the peasant's smock, the carpenter's hat, and all the other regional and traditional clothes of mankind; for the discreet armies of black-coated business men have gone to the ends of the earth. The fashion was born in England along with the industrial revolution; wherever the capitalist system has been established, the London fashion has gone with it.

But the demands of conspicuous consumption remain. Men might escape them, but women could not; attached to each industrious breadwinner was his vicarious consumer; on all public and social occasions it was her task to demonstrate his ability to pay and thus to carry on the battle both for herself and for her husband, and for her the task was even harder than it had been before. For although the actual styles of the new age were not in themselves more unpractical than those of the eighteenth century, the occasions upon which it was essential to appear in ceremonial dress were more numerous and the effort was required of a larger class.

The difference between ceremonial and daily dress in the period which followed the revolutionary and Imperial styles becomes very marked. Daily dress, especially in the mid-nineteenth century, seems designed to shield, to protect the wearer, and to obscure her figure beneath a pyramid, as shapeless as, though more obtuse, than that of Mohammedan women. The face too is hidden by extensive blinkers and the entire get-up is suggestive of a retiring modesty. By night the very opposite effect is obtained by a décolletage suggestive either of extreme leisure or of an imminent collapse of the entire dress.

Despite its occasional variations this fashion is consistent in its very high degree of conspicuous leisure, and it harmonises, both in its modesty and its particular form of outrage, with a romantic and idealistic view of women. To the romantic idealist, woman, that is to say financially reputable woman, is a dead-weight upon society. She is above all things a consumer, she is incapable of any bodily exertion, and requires assistance in the performance of any physical task. She must be handed in and out of carriages, not because she is a person of rank, but because she is debilitated. She is of necessity dependent upon a person of means, and her place is "in the home"; here she produces an expensive family and is frequently in a condition of interesting and costly ill-health. She is trained from girlhood to consume in a decorous manner, to perform difficult tasks of a wholly futile nature called "ladylike accomplishments"; it is something in her favour if her stupidity when confronted by the practical problems of life verges upon complete imbecility. You will find her in the novels of Thackeray, Dickens, and Disraeli, and from a less flattering angle in those of Surtees. It is to be remembered that she existed contemporaneously with women who worked twelve or more hours a day in factories and mines.

This ideal of womanhood, of women that is as instruments of vicarious consumption, dominates the dress of the century; conspicuous outrage is, however, never completely absent and we find, especially in France, another ideal, that of the expensive harlot, which embodies in a different manner the same economic principle. In consequence conspicuous leisure is always a leading characteristic.

We have already spoken of the crinoline, as good a

device for impeding movement as could well be devised, and yet in the latter half of the century fashion obtained the same result by going to the opposite extreme. If we consider the predicament of the lady in Plate 10, we shall perceive that her skirts are so tightly constricted from the waist to below the knee as virtually to forbid loco-motion; secondly, that to make assurance doubly sure she wears a long and inconvenient train; and thirdly, that her corsets impose a permanently rigid position. The total effect is certainly one of extreme leisure.

In the early twentieth century a fashion in some ways resembling that of the First Empire was in vogue; but the devices of conspicuous leisure are inexhaustible; the skirt was fastened about eighteen inches from the hem in such a way as to ensure an immobility as complete as that of the crinoline.

We have become so accustomed to a world of dingy men and bright women that we regard cosmetics or silks upon a man as a sign of effeminacy; the change has been gradual, but very complete. But historically the sumptu-ously dressed man is an artistocrat, a warrior, or a priest, that is to say an ornamental creature of leisure; indeed, as we shall see, this notion is not dead. But the effect of the industrial revolution has been such that with only a few exceptions the dress of men is sober and hard-wearing, and we feel this lack of decorative expenditure to be inherently manly.

The answer to the fifth of the objections proposed in Chapter Three is therefore as follows: the differentiation between the dress of men and that of women which begins through a variation in development throughout the eighteenth century and culminates in the schism of the nineteenth century, arises from the fact that the exhibi-tion of wealth in men no longer depended upon a demon-stration of futility; this change was made possible by the emergence of a wealthy manufacturing class. On the other hand, the women of this class, having no employment and being entrusted with the business of vicarious consumption, continued to follow the sartorial laws already in existence.

*Objection No. 6: Exceptions to Fashion, Archaistic Dress.*— The concept of Vicarious Consumption will also help us to understand various other seemingly anomalous practices, and to remove some of the difficulties presented by our sixth and last objection, for it is not only his wife and his mistress whom the modern producer wishes to see well dressed, there are also his children.

The dressing of very small children gives us an example of vicarious consumption in a very pure form. The "long clothes" of silk, satin, and lace, adorned with ribbons and bibbons on every side, which the children of the very rich may be seen wearing at christenings, etc., are presumably a matter of indifference, or perhaps even of vexation, to those who wear them. Indeed, the pretty clothes of small children generally would seem to be a matter of more pleasure and concern to the parents than to the instruments of display. In pre-industrial society a boy, as soon as he was breeched, wore what was in effect a miniature of adult clothing, even down to the rapier. It was the same with the dress of girls, and these during the industrial era, and until the turn of the nineteenth century, wore clothes not very different to those of their mothers; boys, on the other hand, being neither producers nor yet girls, had to be dressed for vicarious consumption in a new style, masculine, yet different from that of their fathers; a great variety of styles was introduced, varying from kilts and sailor suits to lace-collared imitations of early seventeenth-century dress; there were also various school uniforms of a more or less futile character (see Plate 8).

PLATE 8

Instruments of Vicarious Consumption

Servants no less than children are instruments of
vicarious consumption, especially where their duties
consist mainly in an exhibition of decorative idleness.
As was only to be expected, the nineteenth century which
chastened the dress of the employer left the flunkey in all
his glory; again it is natural that the employé should
be, if anything, grander than before; it was an age of
gorgeous footmen. What is staggering is to find the
bourgeois dressing his servants as aristocrats, to discover
the fashion of Versailles preserved in the Servants' Hall.
Charles II has certainly been avenged in a most decisive
manner. It would be tempting to perceive in this
curious transformation some obscure apprehension of the
class conflict. Tempting, but not, I think, justifiable.
The powdered flunkey was felt to give an aristocratic
air to the household of his employer; he was, as it were, a
piece of period furniture; his livery had, or was supposed
to have, an armigerous significance.

The tendency which we have already noticed, whereby
the more obvious forms of sumptuosity are increasingly
reserved for a large audience alone, and in time come to
be regarded as vulgar in private houses, has affected this
form of vicarious consumption. The liveried man-servant
is almost extinct, even in the most ostentatious houses;
where he survives he adopts an increasingly severe style
of dress. We still expect a butler to look like a gentleman
whatever may be the aspect of his employer, while maid-
servants in cap and apron survive here and there, but
the higher sumptuosity persists only in places of public
entertainment, as in the dress of doormen, waiters, com-
missionaires, and those vicarious consumers who adorn
our cinemas.

The dress of footmen brings us naturally to the subject
of archaism in general; their eighteenth-century aspect
is not an isolated phenomenon, it is characteristic of a

number of survivals which mark the catastrophe of the French and Industrial Revolutions. The change in dress which then occurred was so violent and its revolutionary implications such, that many older people clung to the fashion of the past, letting the young go forward with the new style. It is not surprising, therefore, that many of the survivals which remain or remained with us date from the period immediately preceding those events. They persist as though fossilised by the cataclysm of which they are, in a sense, the memorial. This was the fate of official Court Dress, the dress of jockeys and of lawyers, of the uniform of Chelsea Pensioners, of certain military and naval uniforms, and of various western European peasant costumes. It will be observed that all these, save the last (which are rapidly vanishing as daily wear), are the uniforms of servants, in the broadest sense of the word. Few archaic dresses have altogether resisted the influence of fashion; in the majority of cases archaic clothes are worn only upon ceremonial occasions or for a particular purpose.

It will be found that, although nearly all forms of archaic dress are considered beautiful, "historic", or "old world", none can survive against the emulative process unless some degree of compulsion be applied by an employer (it may be an institution) who can enforce conformity throughout the period when, far from being romantic, they are simply dowdy; and perhaps even this compulsion must at times be assisted by a break in the fashion caused by radical change.

The hardiest survivals are found where the badge of servitude is also a badge of honour. In this connection it is interesting to note that, while several old-established grammar schools in this country have an ancient and sumptuous school-uniform, the fashion in pedagogic wear has been set by Eton; so great indeed has been the

PLATE 9

Archaism

*By courtesy of " The Times "*

social prestige of that institution that for a long time it set the juvenile fashion altogether.

Of the socially reputable professions, two, the Army and the Church, deserve special attention. As has already been pointed out, the sumptuosity of military men is very similar to that of ladies. A certain degree of wasteful expenditure is necessary; so too is a sufficient degree of discomfort and unpracticality (see Plate 10). It is interesting to notice that in both cases the display of pecuniary merit is felt to be particularly glamorous; there is held to be an erotic allure about a full dress uniform just as there is about a fashionable evening gown. The expenditure, the discomfort, the futility, in a word, the high sumptuosity of the former is felt to be particularly manly, in the latter it conveys a notion of feminine fragility. The main difference between them is the much greater conservatism of the military dress.

In considering the evolution of clothes we have seen that conservatism almost always consists in the retention of certain features which in their origin were purely utilitarian but have been made reputable, either by becoming obsolete, as in the case of the guardsman's breastplate, or by being transformed into something so futile as to be no longer recognisable as an object of use. Thus the facings on an infantryman's jacket were originally useful flaps which could be buttoned across to protect the wearer, but, with the adoption of brightly coloured uniforms in the late seventeenth century, they became purely ornamental and were sewn flat upon the jacket. The brightly coloured uniform was once, it would seem, a purely utilitarian device, and no doubt of great service in battles fought at close quarters amidst the smoke of black powder. It would seem to have been Cromwell who put the British soldier into scarlet. But, as the range of fighting increased and with it the value of

PLATE 10

**THE NEW HUSSAR HESSIANS AND PANTS.**

"SEE, I'VE DROPPED MY HANDKERCHIEF, CAPTAIN DE VERE!"
"I KNOW YOU HAVE, MISS CONSTANCE. I'M VERY SORRY. I
CAN'T STOOP, EITHER!"

Conspicuous Leisure: feminine and military.
*From 'Punch', May 25, 1878*

concealment, there arose a difference of opinion between those who regarded war primarily as an occasion for conspicuous consumption and those who took a purely utilitarian view. The latter party exclaimed at the enormous bearskin, the tight collar which strangled the infantryman before he could come to grips with the foe, the glitter of polished buttons, the glare of pipeclay which made so clear a target for the opposing marksman, and the extreme constriction of the uniform, which at one time was so great in the British army that the life-guards were unable to perform their sword exercise.[1] The conservatives replied that the exact and expensive apparatus of war, the brilliant colours and strict cere-monial of the parade ground, were essential to discipline. The soldier might be killed by his uniform, but with-out it he would surely lose his self-respect. The true argument, I believe, was not really military at all but aesthetic or moral. It was based upon the view that military splendour is a thing good and beautiful in itself, and that if wars were not to be fought in style they had better not be fought at all.

It was only very slowly that military fashions changed and even then it was usually as the result of bloody disasters upon the field of battle, nor can it be said even today that the demands of sumptuosity do not sometimes prevail over those of military necessity.[2]

As with civilians so with soldiers, the inconveniences of sumptuous dress have to some extent been met by the adoption of occasional uniforms, and most armies now have one style for ceremonies and another for military operations. The practice of making a soldier carry a special change of clothing for grand occasions dates, I

[1] See C. F. Atkinson's article on "Uniforms", *Encyclopædia Britannica*, 11th Ed. Also *Punch* for June 3rd, 1854.
[2] See Wintringham, *Freedom is Our Weapon*, 1941.

believe, from the eighteenth century, and today a general wears his full regalia as seldom as a bishop.

The wearing of appropriate clothes has been so important a part of devout observances for so long a time that it is very difficult to speak of religious clothes without trespassing upon the dangerous ground of theology. The priest is known by his cloth and this has usually been an instrument of conspicuous leisure. Veblen sees therein simply the livery of God's service and there can be no doubt that there is much truth in this view. In their various ways the Churches have provided the greatest vehicle for futile expenditure in the history of the world. Along with the desire to propitiate and honour the Deity there has frequently been a particular delight in the exhibition of wealth, whether by an individual or by a community, in the building and servicing of houses for God, that is to say for an economically futile purpose. To this end not only have great treasures been amassed and great institutions endowed, but an army of ministers has been supported by the sacrifices of the faithful; these persons are thus, in a sense, in the ornamental position of flunkeys or women. There is, however, another tendency in established religious institutions which makes of the priest a *rentier*, a man of property and of fashion. This tendency, which is natural enough where a strong vested interest is concerned, is repugnant to those who have found the money, not for an individual, but for God.[1] Again and again throughout the Middle Ages we find contemporary moralists complaining that the clergy dress in secular fashion; despite many attempts at reform this practice continues up to and beyond the time of the Reformation. From a sumptuary point of view that movement is important, in that it led the Roman Church to make strenuous efforts to impose sartorial discipline

[1] See 1 Samuel ii, 12-16.

upon her priests, and among the Protestants to an abolition of purple and fine linen, *i.e.* to the abolition of conspicuous consumption, which in the case of the extreme Protestant sects was effected by the abolition of priesthood as a whole-time job. In neither case did the reformers wholly fail or entirely succeed. Among the older Churches we find wigged and powdered ecclesiastics until the time of the French Revolution, at which point the Roman Church appears to have undergone that process of fossilisation to which we have already alluded. Amongst the Protestants, especially where a vested interest was established and the clergyman became genteel, we usually find some kind of modified uniform, which, however, is by no means immune to the emulative process.

The effect of this double process of enrichment and reform is to make ecclesiastical dress a fascinating museum of past modes. In the Roman Church we find vestigial forms of the pallium and the dalmatica, in the dress of some orders the costume of the dark ages, in that of others the extravagant head-dresses of the late fifteenth century, while the fashions of the Renaissance are commemorated in Geneva bands and dog collars.

The dress of the Church of England is a compromise, and in this Church we find also a very marked differentiation between ceremonial and workaday dress. The Established Church, and she alone it would seem, has been affected by that tendency of fashion which we have called Conspicuous Outrage. The fashion arose during the 'thirties of the last century and took the form of a more and more daring imitation of Roman vestments. Like every other fashion it caused scandal, and like every other ended by becoming perfectly respectable.

The fashionability of Rome in Protestant countries is, of course, no mere matter of dress. In that it is an ancient cult, providing large opportunities for conspicuous consumption, the Roman Church has attracted the higher income groups in Protestant countries, ever since she ceased to be a political rival or an economic temptation. This has been particularly the case in those countries where the middle classes have established inexpensive and vulgar sects, and in which, therefore, the older ceremonies gain by contrast. The quality of fashionable outrage is intensified by the license which the Roman Church, and in particular the Society of Jesus, is supposed to permit the individual in sexual and other modish indulgences. These manifest advantages seem to have been largely offset in countries such as the United States, where Roman Catholicism is peculiarly the religion of the poor.

It is in the light of these subtler manifestations of conspicuous outrage, as also of more intellectual considerations, that we should judge the movement which shook Oxford and the Church in the last century.

The foregoing examples of archaism are all in a large measure the product of Vicarious Consumption; there is, however, another kind of archaism which is of quite different origin. At the very centre of the whirligig of fashion one may perceive a point which seems almost motionless. There are people whose station is so very exalted, whose social claims are so obviously beyond all question, that they can remain largely, if not entirely, immune to the demands of fashion; to them the emulative process is scarcely applicable; they can, in consequence, be as completely lacking in sumptuosity as they please. To the millionaire or the crowned head all sins are forgiven (see Plate 9). This clearly is one of those exceptions that prove the rule.

*PLATE II*

Fashions for 1894

# CHAPTER SEVEN

# RECENT TRENDS

Where do these grand new winter sports beauty boxes come from? They are the brainchild of Cyclax: and contain a complete Romany Tan make-up, protective Day Lotion, powder, rouge, lipstick and nail enamel, and a tube of Beauty Bronze. The outfit is made up in two sizes, for a two-week or a four-week trip at 25s. 6d. and 32s. 6d. And for your romantic, pink night make-up, Cyclax have nice coffrets of lipstick, rouge, and nail enamel to match (14s. 6d. complete) for you to take abroad in your favourite shade.

*Vogue*, December 14th, 1938

I THINK it may be claimed that the foregoing application of Veblen's *The Theory of the Leisure Class* provides an account of the development of fashion which, though necessarily rough and incomplete, gives a sufficient answer to our objections.

In each case we have found that the history of fashionable dress is tied to that of the resurgent middle class and the emulative process to which that class gave birth. Given these two connected causes, the European origin and subsequent diffusion of fashion are readily comprehensible, so too the similarity of development wherever a similarity of class structure exists. In the same way the radical effect of the struggles between the bourgeoisie and the aristocracy is both obvious and necessary. If we can also admit the theory of Vicarious Consumption, the schism between masculine and feminine clothes takes its place naturally in the same process as does the persistence of certain archaistic forms. Implicit in the whole is a system of sartorial morality dependent upon pecuniary standards of value.

There are, however, certain recent trends in the history of dress which cannot at first sight be reconciled with this explanation, and which have, I believe, done much harm to Veblen as a philosopher of clothes.

When Veblen wrote *The Theory of the Leisure Class*, feminine fashion was very strong in its emphasis upon Conspicuous Leisure; skirts trailed, the waist was constricted to its minimum, and the invertebrate appearance was emphasised by wide sleeves or a cape. The neck line had begun that upward movement which was to end in a prodigious display of leisurely discomfort near the ears (see Plate 11). But within thirty years the fashion had changed very considerably, and for both sexes. The feminine dress of about the year 1928 was a sack-like envelope which left arms and neck free, terminated in a kilt, and reduced the feminine silhouette to a flat tube. The laws of Conspicuous Waste and Conspicuous Consumption seemed to have gone by the board.

The fashion of the late 1920's does not, however, represent so complete a break with sumptuosity as might be supposed. At no point has the display of wealth been abandoned; furs, jewels, and expensive materials have kept their usual place, the abbreviated skirt performed two of the functions of sumptuosity. As it receded it displayed an increasingly outrageous amount of leg, at the same time it guaranteed the possession of expensive silk stockings and completely futile high-heeled shoes.

The point of maximum brevity was reached about 1928 and then a highly significant thing happened: skirts for the evening went down, those for the day remained put, or nearly so (despite the efforts of the dressmakers). I think that this gives us the clue to an understanding of the processes at work.

Before pursuing this matter further it is perhaps necessary to say something about the idea, which has

PLATE 12

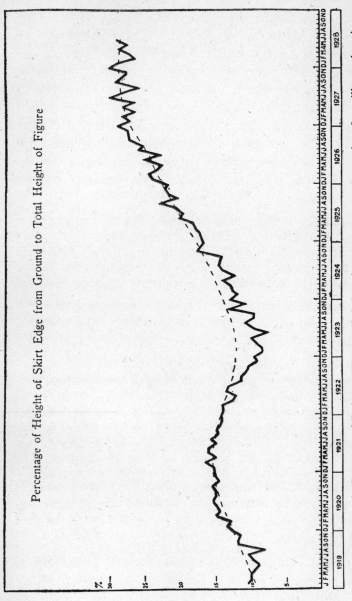

Percentage of Height of Skirt Edge from Ground to Total Height of Figure

From Nystrom's *Economics of Fashion*. The graph is based upon measurements taken from illustrations in fashion papers. Nystrom considers that "the irregularities of the graph . . . are probably due to errors of prediction and illustration in the fashion magazines rather than representative of actual changes in fashion trend. It is believed that the real fashion trend might be most truthfully represented by a smoothed curve indicated by the dotted line."

received wide credence, that this youthful and exiguous style was a direct outcome of the Four Years' War. This view has gained the support both of Mr. Laver and of Liddel Hart, the great military historian.

Beginning with the statement (to which we have already taken exception) that: "A great War nearly always has a profound effect on feminine costume", Mr. Laver points to the shortening of skirts during the war and to the emergence thereafter of a very youthful fashion, the result, he suggests, of the emancipation of the younger woman, who had obtained her freedom during the war years.

For probably the first time in history the flapper was free, and it was she who was to dictate the fashion for the next decade. If anyone doubts this let him consider the extremely juvenile form which women's dress suddenly adopted in the nineteen-twenties, culminating in the little girl's dress of 1926.[1]

This, however, is not all; there is a second connected theory which deals with the disappearance of corsets; it is as follows:

It is a curious fact in human history, and one well worthy of more attention than it has received from the social psychologists, that the disappearance of corsets is always accompanied by two related phenomena—promiscuity and an inflated currency. No corsets, bad money, and general moral laxity; corsets, sound money, and the prestige of the *grande cocotte*—such seems to be the rule. In any case, the period immediately following the Great War showed a marked resemblance to the Directoire period, when also women flung their corsets into the dustbin and their bonnets over the windmills.

The disappearance of corsets is connected with another phenomenon characteristic of all periods following a great upheaval. The first thing (not necessarily the second or the third thing) which the emancipated woman does is to try to look as much like a man as possible. She therefore tends to cut her hair short and to abandon any pretence of having a waist.[2]

[1] Laver, *op. cit.* chap. ix, p. 122.    [2] *Ibid.* p. 125.

PLATE 13

Fashions for July 1914
*As seen in ' Vogue '*

Now the unavoidable difficulty about this explanation is the great time-lag which exists between the supposed cause and the effect. The radical breakaway from long skirts, and conspicuous leisure generally, begins at earliest in 1924 (see Plate 12), that is to say six years after the armistice and at the end of the period of extreme inflation. What then was the emancipated woman up to in the interval? Mr. Laver is far too good an historian not to recognise and to admit the difficulty; indeed, with his eyes fixed upon the sartorial effects of war, he expresses some natural surprise that the change in fashions did not occur during the course of hostilities; his answer is:

So long as a great upheaval is in progress the variations which it introduces are hidden from the eyes of those who are undergoing it. Just as it was not until after the death of Robespierre that the changes in social structure which the French Revolution had introduced became reflected in women's clothes, so it was not until after the conclusion of the War that the very profound changes which the conflict had brought into being became apparent.[1]

This, it will be remembered, was not the case in the Puritan Revolution, where the process was if anything reversed; but even if we ignore this positive case, and also all those wars and revolutions which have produced no fashionable change, the statement is still far from providing us with a comprehensible explanation.

If now we look at Plates 13, 14, and 15, it will appear that the slackening of the waistline and the straightening of the silhouette had already begun before the war; Poiret had made it his object.[2] These tendencies develop at an accelerated speed, but without a break, up to and after the armistice. In other words, the fashions

[1] Laver, *op. cit.* p. 123-4.
[2] Poiret, *op. cit.* p. 63. See also Price, who remarks upon the extreme youthfulness of contemporary (1913) fashions.

*PLATE 14*

Fashions for late June 1924
*As seen in ' Vogue '*

of the early 'twenties are not very different from those of the years immediately preceding the Four Years' War.[1]

It may, however, be argued that the emancipation of women was already under way and was only accelerated by the conflict, and this I believe is true and provides a part, but only a part, of our answer. The essential change is to be found in a new attitude to feminine futility, a reflection perhaps of her improved status. Woman is no longer regarded as an agent for vicarious consumption; in a sense, of course, she has always been a consumer on her own account, but now she has taken her place alongside her brothers as an active exponent of futility.

Men, it has been said, have for long practised various violent physical exercises of an uneconomic nature as a part of their social duties and these have exerted a great influence on their entire wardrobe. We have noted the survival of an archaistic uniform in the conspicuously wasteful ceremony of fox-hunting; perhaps we may ascribe the preservation of the kilt to the influence of those expensive sports which are best undertaken in the Highlands. Masculine dress, in so far as it has developed since the middle of the last century, has been changed almost entirely through the reflected influence of outdoor sports. This would not seem to be, as Veblen suggests, because of the particular merit attaching to personal prowess and the competitive spirit. It is not competition which makes a sport fashionable but expense, and indeed it is from sports which are not directly competitive that the majority of our masculine fashions are derived. The

[1] The abbreviated skirt certainly showed more leg in 1919 than in 1914, nevertheless even this supposedly typical "post-war" style is of "pre-war" origin; in the spring of 1914 a committee of ladies in Paris protested against the prevalent fashion which exposed the leg completely to view. See Fischel and von Boehn, iv, 123.

"boater", the "deer stalker", and the "Norfolk jacket", to name a few of the articles of clothing which derive from sports, have been adopted because they are associated with expensive and purely wasteful pursuits. The directly competitive sports suffer in esteem because they tend to become professionalised and thus acquire a rational economic motive. Highly commercialised sports such as boxing and football have in fact come to be considered slightly vulgar and have set no fashions. Horse racing is of particular interest in that the spectators, who lose money, set many fashions; while the bookmakers, who make money, set none.

The view that the respectability of a sport depends mainly upon the opportunity which it provides for futile expenditure is strongly borne out by the fact that among the best considered sports of this century are those which involve, not only an expensive outfit, but an expensive journey in search of suitable conditions. Thus we find that an energetic but aimless expenditure of time and money on the slopes of the Alps or the mud banks of the Adriatic became almost a part of the routine of fashion.

It will be seen, therefore, that there is no pecuniary impropriety in the participation in active sports by women. The only objection thereto is that they may appear to be wasting money on their own account and not for the good repute of their owners. With the gradual improvement in the status of women this objection was withdrawn; the opportunity was eagerly taken, for it involved not only a futile expenditure of time, but the provision of a more various wardrobe. The riding-habit had for long been a part of a gentlewoman's paraphernalia, but riding, like croquet, allows a certain measure of repose. Late in the nineteenth century the attempt was made to conserve the fashions of leisure with the practice of more energetic sports. The effect was grotesque, and was very similar to those earlier attempts of men to do likewise, as, for instance, to play cricket in top-hats. Nevertheless, the effort to combine the incompatibles continues right up to and after the Great War; finally it broke down and in so doing combined neatly with the prevalent mode of Conspicuous Outrage, which consisted, not, as in previous ages, in a projection of the waist, the buttocks, and the bust, but in a flaunting of the legs; the two tendencies go hand in hand and with them the contemporary ideal of the boyish (*i.e.* athletic) figure. At the height of the mode, woman was a spartiate; she showed it in her dress just as seventeenth-century man showed that he was a soldier; it need hardly be said that in both cases there was much unjustifiable pretence. But the athlete in the ballroom was almost as grotesque as the professional beauty on the tennis court. The solution, therefore, was just the same as that arrived at at the time of the industrial revolution: one style, that of futile exercise, is used for day wear; another, that of futile repose, serves for the evening (see Plate 16.)

This mode favours the proletariat as against the middle class, just as a similar change in masculine dress favoured the bourgeoisie as against the aristocracy in the eighteenth century; it enables the working woman to carry on her daily tasks with less discomfort and still perform her ceremonial functions with an air of conspicuous leisure.

Perhaps the most illustrative and remarkable feature of recent trends has been the fashion in cosmetics. In the eighteenth century both paint and powder were favoured, but were, I suspect, to a large extent a part of the apparatus of the aristocracy in its defiance of the middle classes. At all events, with the triumph of the latter, cosmetics were not only abandoned but con-

PLATE 15

Fashions for 1927. *By courtesy of Messrs. Harrods*

demned, and their use, on honest women, was surreptitious and imitative. In our own time they have returned as a form of outrage comparable to short skirts and bad language, and have rapidly become so customary as to be respectable. Indeed it is scarcely thought decent today for a young woman to attend an important function with her face unpainted. There is in consequence little artifice, little deceit, in the customary decoration of the face and finger-nails; the intention is clear and unequivocal.

The great innovation of the century has been the adoption of a new standard of beauty in pigmentation. Hitherto the ideal had been one of shaded and unfreckled fairness; sunburn was felt to imply a healthy industrious open-air life, tolerable perhaps in a man [1] but not in a lady. But in the 'twenties the woman who could prove that she was no city worker, but one of those able to bask in the sunlight of the Mediterranean, was esteemed for her tan just as her grandmother had been for her pallor. Thus we find the rare spectacle of women powdering themselves brown when unable to roast themselves to the same end. With the division of modes referred to above, it became necessary to exhibit two complexions, the sporting sunburn by day, the delicate pallor by night; the one indicative of Conspicuous Consumption, the other of Conspicuous Leisure.

Viewed in this light, recent trends assumed an aspect which is by no means incompatible with the basic theories of Veblen.

[1] But see the opinions of Sir Walter Elliot in *Persuasion*

PLATE *16*

Day and evening styles for December 1938
(Compare these with those shown in Plate 11)
*As seen in ' Vogue ', December 1938*

# CHAPTER EIGHT

# DEVIATIONS FROM VEBLEN
# —AESTHETICS OF DRESS

"Il n'y a de beau que les étoffes roulées sur le corps et drapées, dit
Gamelin. Tout ce qui a été taillé et cousu est affreux."

Ces pensées, mieux placées dans un livre de Winckelman que dans
la bouche d'un homme qui parle à des Parisiennes, furent rejetées
avec le mépris de l'indifférence.

ANATOLE FRANCE, *Les Dieux ont soif*

IF there be any novelty in this brief introduction to the
study of finery it lies in those parts thereof which imply
or express a contradiction of Veblen's theory.

In this chapter I propose to consider two cardinal points
of disagreement and for this purpose have extracted
quotations from *The Theory of the Leisure Class* which appear
to me to contain untenable arguments. It must not be
imagined that these extracts give a fair sample of Veblen's
thought, they are indeed singularly unrepresentative, and
have been selected simply with a view to bringing out
fundamental disagreements. Veblen's theory can only
be judged on a complete examination.

The value of Veblen as a philosopher of clothes lies in
his economic approach to his subject, an approach which
leads him directly to the formulation of those illuminating
theories of social behaviour which he calls the Laws of
Conspicuous Consumption, Vicarious Consumption, and
Conspicuous Leisure. He fails, so it seems to me, to
explain the history of dress when he relies upon notions
which are not derived from economics, and when his
attention has been too closely engaged by the conditions

of his own time and country. Both these elements would appear to have moved him in the following explanation of the difference which then existed between the dress of men and that of women:

At the stage of economic development at which the women were still in the full sense the property of the men, the performance of conspicuous leisure and consumption came to be part of the services required of them. The women being not their own masters, obvious expenditure and leisure on their part would redound to the credit of their master rather than to their own credit; and therefore the more expensive and the more obviously unproductive the women of the household are, the more creditable and the more effective for the purpose of the reputability of the household or its head will their life be. So much so that the women have been required not only to afford evidence of a life of leisure, but even to disable themselves for useful activity.

It is at this point that the dress of men falls short of that of women, and for a sufficient reason. Conspicuous waste and conspicuous leisure are reputable because they are evidence of pecuniary strength; pecuniary strength is reputable or honorific because, in the last analysis, it argues success and superior force; therefore the evidence of waste and leisure put forth by any individual in his own behalf cannot consistently take such a form or be carried to such a pitch as to argue incapacity or marked discomfort on his part; as the exhibition would in that case show not superior force, but inferiority, and so defeat its own purpose. So, then, wherever wasteful expenditure and the show of abstention from effort is normally, or on an average, carried to the extent of showing obvious discomfort or voluntarily induced physical disability, there the immediate inference is that the individual in question does not perform this wasteful expenditure and undergo this disability for her own personal gain in pecuniary repute, but in behalf of someone else to whom she stands in a relation of economic dependence; a relation which in the last analysis must, in economic theory, reduce itself to a relation of servitude.

To apply this generalisation to women's dress, and put the matter in concrete terms: the high heel, the skirt, the impracticable bonnet, the corset, and the general disregard of the wearer's comfort which is an obvious feature of all civilised women's apparel, are so many items of evidence to the effect that in the modern civilised scheme of life the woman is still, in theory, the economic dependent of the man,—that, perhaps in a highly idealised sense, she is still the man's chattel.[1]

Historically this is not tenable. Indeed where women are reduced entirely to the role of chattels and a man's wealth is counted by the number of his wives, it is he, rather than she, who displays wealth upon the person. The mere act of feeding and maintaining a seraglio is enough in the world's eyes, and the inmates are private property for private use. The demands of sartorial morality do, no doubt, impose a high degree of sumptuosity within the harem (just as they do in underclothes). But polygamous man is certainly not less, and probably much more ornate, in his appearance than his monogamous fellow. It is when women begin to acquire status on their own that they begin to dress for the world; even so, in the earlier, the feudal stages, it is the men, not the women, who lead the fashion and are the first to adopt a new style. Any survey of the history of fashion will show that the extremes of conspicuous leisure are common to both sexes; men have worn just those garments which Veblen considers particularly feminine, and they are typical of feudal dress. Veblen's basic theory is, however, perfectly correct in that the noble, like the lady, was supposed to be incapable of manual labour. The difference, as we have seen, arises when a certain amount of work is no longer socially disreputable; it is then, and only then, that the corset and the high heel become effeminate.

The misconception would seem to arise from an attempt to apply certain essentially nineteenth-century characteristics of fashion to the history of dress as a whole.

[1] *The Theory of the Leisure Class*, pp. 180-82.

But their is another and deeper cause. Veblen is preoccupied with individuals, or families, rather than with classes; he is obsessed by the notion of personal prowess, which, I think, leads him astray in the field of sport, and he sees the main impulse as one of the individual or head of a family demonstrating his pecuniary strength through dress and thus maintaining the "good repute" of the household.

But the whole theory breaks down if we do not allow the claims of "class solidarity" to be greater than those of individuals or families. For if the business of demonstrating pecuniary strength be regarded simply as a household parade before the world, there is nothing to prevent, and indeed much to encourage, each householder to adopt his own fashion; such eccentricity would have the supreme merit of avoiding the imputation of cheapness which must lie against all mass-produced goods. But in fact, although a certain degree of singularity is encouraged for this very reason (as for instance in the choice of women's hats), for another reason it is always subordinated to the standards of a class. Nothing is worse than too much originality in dress, and it will be found that individual prowess is severely held in bounds by the necessary uniformity of the mode. It may be safely asserted that the usual desire of the great majority of those who follow fashion is not so much to achieve personal distinction as to arrive at a happy mean and to merge discreetly into a distinguished class. Sumptuous dress is of necessity a kind of class uniform which forbids prowess, and this is especially the case where, as in pre-revolutionary China, the social structure is of a rigid and unchanging kind; here individual taste and fantasy are brought to a minimum; there is a universal sameness within each class which can hardly be altered, save by the introduction of a new class system.

What would appear to be an even more fundamental cleavage is revealed by Veblen's account of mutation:

The standard of reputability requires that dress should show wasteful expenditure; but all wastefulness is offensive to native taste. The psychological law has already been pointed out that all men—and women perhaps even in a higher degree—abhor futility, whether of effort or of expenditure; much as Nature was once said to abhor a vacuum. But the principle of conspicuous waste requires an obvious futile expenditure; and *the resulting conspicuous expensiveness of dress is therefore intrinsically ugly.* . . . The ostensible usefulness of the fashionable details of dress, however, is always so transparent a make-believe, and their substantial futility presently forces itself so baldly upon our attention as to become unbearable, and then we take refuge in a new style. But the new style must conform to the requirements of reputable wastefulness and futility. Its futility presently becomes as odious as that of its predecessor; and the only remedy which the law of waste allows us is to seek relief in some new construction, equally futile and equally untenable. *Hence the essential ugliness and unceasing change of fashionable attire.*

Having so explained the phenomenon of shifting fashions, the next thing is to make it tally with everyday facts. Among these everyday facts is the well-known liking which all men have for the styles that are in vogue at any given time. A new style comes into vogue and remains in favour for a season, and, at least so long as it is a novelty, people very generally find the new style attractive. *The prevailing fashion is felt to be beautiful.* This is due partly to the relief it affords in being different from what went before it, partly to its being reputable. As indicated in the last chapter, the canon of reputability to some extent shapes our tastes, so that under its guidance anything will be accepted as becoming until its novelty wears off, or until the warrant of reputability is transferred to a new and novel structure serving the same general purpose. That the alleged beauty, or "loveliness", of the styles in vogue at any given time is transient and spurious only is attested by the fact that none of the many shifting fashions will bear the test of time. When seen in the perspective of half a dozen years or more, the best of our fashions strike us as grotesque, if not unsightly. Our transient attachment to whatever happens to be the latest rests on other than aesthetic grounds, and lasts only until our abiding aesthetic sense has had time to assert itself and reject this latest indigestible contrivance.[1]

This passage may serve to show how much this essay owes to Veblen and how far it deviates. Here again the actual history of fashion contradicts Veblen's explanation; this it does in two manners—first in the mode of evolution, secondly in the history of the forms selected.

If we return to the example of mutation taken in Chapter Four we shall see that neither the crinoline nor the voluminous petticoats which it replaced had any ostensible usefulness, nor indeed does any full-length skirt; as Veblen says: "It is expensive and it hampers the wearer at every turn and incapacitates her for all useful exertion ".[2] (This statement implies that nearly all European fashions for women contain a large element of futility and hence of ugliness.) Now the additional futility of the crinoline became apparent quite early in its history; as we have noticed, it forced itself baldly upon the attention of the Empress of the French as early as 1860. The reply was, first to make it larger still, then gradually to gather it backwards into a train, which became a bustle. But the kind of change which we should expect, given Veblen's aesthetic laws, would be a rapid jump away from this species of futility to something quite different, the Directoire style perhaps.

Veblen's history is as unsatisfactory in explaining why the mode sometimes turns towards simplicity as it is in explaining why it usually moves in the opposite sense. On three occasions, as we have seen, the fashion has changed in the direction of increased simplicity, in 1642

---

[1] Veblen, *op. cit.* pp. 176-8. My italics. It should, however, be added that in many other passages Veblen is far from rejecting the emulative process. The aesthetic theory here given would seem to be a kind of supererogatory theory.

[2] *Ibid.* p. 171.

and 1789 the change was more or less transitory, in the industrial revolution it was almost permanent; no universal aesthetic sentiment can be applied to such seemingly inconsequent behaviour; a constant influence will surely produce a constant phenomenon, which fashion is not. Once again we are forced to admit the paramount importance of classes, in this instance class struggles, without which the history of fashion is inexplicable. It is only through a study of emulation, and of the effect of revolutionary crises upon the emulative process, that we can understand fashion in its stages of critical development.

This quotation also brings us to a cleavage of even more fundamental importance. According to Veblen the prevailing mode is only "felt to be beautiful", in fact its beauty is spurious, as is the beauty of all fashions. Oscar Wilde took the same view when he said: "After all, what is fashion? it is usually a form of ugliness so intolerable that we have to alter it every six months".[1]

Like Wilde and like Watts, Veblen is deeply affected by the discovery which we must all make in modern society of the odiousness of yesterday's fashions; therefore he turns naturally to an ideal of unchanging excellence, and this ideal is perhaps hellenic, certainly it is what we should now call "functional". If the beauty of dress be measured against any such absolute standard, the pecuniary canons of taste will certainly be found wanting; all sumptuous, and therefore all fashionable, dress must be condemned and we are of necessity driven to admit the "essential ugliness" of fashionable attire, and thence to the statement that its charm is spurious, "it is only felt to be beautiful".

But can we in truth say more of a beautiful object than that we feel it to be beautiful? Does not such a state-

[1] Wilde, *Suitable Dress for Women Workers*.

ment go as far as we can go in recommending a work of art? If we are to accept Veblen's evidence as it stands, perhaps we should rather say that only the prevailing fashion is beautiful. Either way we are forced back upon a position which is untenable in the light of general experience; in the presence of the fashions of the past six hundred years there are few who will condemn all as ugly, and it is only in the case of the immediate past and the immediate present that anything remotely resembling general agreement will be found, the former being frightful, the latter charming. Nor has there yet been a fashion which has not been judged in both manners; the crinoline was admired in its time, condemned in the age of bustles, and again admired after three-quarters of a century.

As Baudelaire has pointed out, there are two elements in beauty, the one permanent the other fugitive.[1] A hat new from Paris is lovely because it is new from Paris; had it crossed the Channel twenty-five years ago it would be hideous. That is the sincere view of most women who buy hats.

In opposition to this view we have that of the "pure artist", who, in theory, is capable of perceiving all the intrinsic charm of a shop-soiled remnant of twenty-five years back, and of judging upon its merits alone the latest and most enchanting creation of a Parisian milliner. This latter attitude, which may, in a sense, be called "impressionist", supposes an unmoved contemplation of the *décor* of modern life, in which the influence of fashion counts for nothing. There is also a third view which has its importance in the history of dress and which may loosely be termed "romantic". To the romantic the actual world of fashion is horrid, he turns

---

[1] See his study of the work of Guys, *Le Peintre de la Vie moderne*, p. 24, in the English translation of Konody.

from it in so far as he is able, and seeks consolation in the contemplation of a distant or imaginary world from which the vulgarity of the present is excluded.

I do not think that either of these attitudes, in so far as they are manifested in the appreciation or artistic representation of costume, would have been comprehensible to a painter of the T'ang period or to an Italian of the fourteenth century. To them in their social circumstances the problem would not have presented itself. They have by our standards no sense of time.

Thus the Primitive could depict the Virgin Mary in the latest and most fashionable dress of his period, while the modern artist who did likewise would be thought blasphemous or affected, and would moreover suffer some inconvenience when his sitter's gown went out of fashion.

The complete acceptance of the fashion of the age is only possible where, as in China or Mediaeval Europe, social change is so gradual that sartorial change is barely noticeable. The gradual increase in the rate of change leads to a gradual stabilisation of the attire of deities, etc. First God, then His Family, then the Saints, and finally almost any ideal figure, such as Britannia or Uncle Sam, acquires a garment which is either timeless or historic. It is interesting to note that most ideal figures are expected to display a fairly high degree of conspicuous leisure in their attire and that this applies even to the Creator; His Family is less completely identified with a life of Honourable Futility than He, though even here a high degree of sumptuosity is felt to be proper.

The sense of anachronism in religion, which begins about the time of Rembrandt,[1] takes its form from Classical antiquity; later, in the nineteenth century, a

[1] Or earlier in the case of the Italians, see the very just observations of Sir Joshua Reynolds in his Fourth Discourse.

mediaeval style is adopted. Now "antiquity", especially when it is copied from Greco-Roman models, is not wanting in sumptuosity. In the Pompeian and even in the Egyptian styles there is nothing to shock the pecuniary standards of taste; the standards of skilled labour remain. It was by these standards that beauty was judged by wearer and artist alike prior to the industrial revolution. Vulgarity then implied crude coloration, imperfections in texture, and a low degree of finish generally. But with the invention of competent machinery it became possible to turn out highly finished artifacts at a very low price; at the same time and for the same reason the peasant weaver, needlewoman, or fuller, was driven out of existence; the work when once it had become scarce became valuable. The much greater amount of labour put into peasant work of all kinds sent its price soaring above that of the more highly finished products of the factory. This change in productive costs is reflected in a corresponding change in aesthetic valuation. The home-made product of the loom was soon felt to be picturesquely beautiful, it was the factory product which became vulgar. The romantic, and more particularly the Pre-Raphaelite aesthetic, is, so far as clothes are concerned, a product of this revaluation. But it also results from another feature of the machine age, for now the fashion exerts its influence over a much greater section of society. In consequence the *décor* of modern life has been deeply influenced, not by the current fashion, but by that which has just vanished, than which nothing could be more odious to a person of sensitive tastes. To the aesthete the masses are repellent, not because they are unfashionable but because they are out of fashion; the clothes of the people are a cheap imitation of the late mode. The aesthete must therefore take refuge, either in those places in which a low degree of industrialisation has retarded the emulative process, or in an imaginary world untroubled by the march of time; here he can be happy in "old world surroundings", *i.e.* amidst expensive productive processes in which craftsmanship still rules supreme.

The logical outcome of this attitude was the socialism of William Morris, the attempt to change an aesthetically odious world. The actual effect of the Pre-Raphaelite workshops was widely different, that which had been intended to beautify the lives of the poor became the esoteric cult of the rich. The insistence upon expensive methods of production and the prestige attaching to a new aesthetic cult produced an "aesthetic" style of dress, a rather shapeless mode which for a time competed with Paris. But in becoming the fashion this dress reform movement failed; the process of emulation and vulgarisation ensued. The aesthetes had attempted to apply an absolute canon of beauty to dress; they succeeded only in creating a fashion.

The opposite and bolder attitude, that of the observer who accepts the world with all its cheapness and vulgarity, who neither revels in the fashions as did Van Dyck, nor rejects them like Burne Jones, has of course of its very nature no direct effect on dress. Nevertheless a certain influence made its way from the world of aesthetic innovations into that of fashion, and to a limited extent into that of dress design.

The revaluation of productive processes made possible a more catholic appreciation of the arts than was possible to those who were bound to an acceptance of the supreme merit of highly finished work. The art of ancient China, of India, Japan, Persia, and the near East, became acceptable by degrees to all, but to the newer school of aesthetes the work of the Primitives, the Byzantines, the Copts, and of very rude peoples, was open.

When modern painting, inspired by these newer standards of taste, was first shown to the British public, there was an outcry. The same people who accepted the crudities of thirteenth-century work could not permit the same kind of thing from their contemporaries; the former had, after all, the value which attached to rare and historical objects, but for the latter there could be no excuse; the painters who produced them were wilfully defrauding the public of the finished dexterity to which it felt entitled from an artist who had received an expensive training. "My little girl, aged nine, could have done that", they exclaimed, implying that the amount of labour put into the production of the works concerned was totally insufficient.

So monstrous a breach of custom was of course felt to be obscene; it was not, therefore, very long before it became fashionable. How could the vulgar ever hope to understand anything so abstruse? Here was something so remote from the machine-made artifact, such a slap in the face to tradition, that it could safely be adopted by the well-to-do. M. Paul Poiret, a designer of genius, allied himself with the new movement; he gained the help of M. Dufy, who translated the new style into textiles, and of the Russian Ballet, which clothed the new movement in a proper cloak of sumptuosity. The fashions of the time were largely dependent upon Conspicuous Outrage and to this the "modern" movement in aesthetics, "cubism", the use of negro or Polynesian *motifs*, etc., made a certain contribution. Nevertheless the abandonment of all ordinary standards of pecuniary taste has always been a serious drawback where this kind of aesthetic influence has been exerted upon the applied arts. The influence of the more advanced cultures, more advanced that is to say from a technical point of view, has always been much more potent.

This enquiry into the nature of aesthetic judgments on dress has led us rather far from our subject, but it will serve to remind the reader of the numerous allied fashions to which Veblen's theory may, and indeed has, been applied. There are fashions in speech, in manners, in decoration, even in learning, which may perhaps be subject to those influences which we have found to affect the development of dress. The whole texture of European civilisation has changed along with the changes in the clothes of Europeans, and fashions in dress are only part of a much greater process. At the same time it would appear that these fashions are themselves of the utmost importance in determining the aesthetic, sexual, and historical character of an age; our whole conception of the world must surely be deeply influenced by the changing appearance of our fellow creatures and the changing demands of sartorial morality. To determine the nature of that evolutionary process is therefore a matter of no small historical interest; I am convinced that whatever modifications it may be necessary to make in his theory, it is Veblen who has shown us the true manner of approaching the problem. I do not see how any serious student of social history can afford to neglect his teachings. It may therefore be useful, though perhaps tedious, to recapitulate. In the following summary I have italicised that which is not explicit in *The Theory of the Leisure Class*:

(1) Dress serves purposes which are both utilitarian and spiritual or moral; generally speaking, and especially in the higher ranks of any society, the "goodness" of any garment is of more account than its utilitarian value.

(2) The goodness of any given dress is a matter of concern to those to whom the dress belongs, whether the owner be the wearer or not (vicarious consumption).

(3) Good dress is sumptuous; sumptuosity depends upon the demonstration of expenditure or of an expensive way of life; this is obtained in the following manners:

(*a*) By the use of expensive materials or expensive productive processes (conspicuous consumption).

(*b*) By being made in such a manner as to suggest a more or less unproductive manner of life (conspicuous leisure).

(*c*) By being designed in such a manner as to suggest that the wearer indulges in reputable (futile) activities (conspicuous waste).

(*d*) *By being designed in such a manner as to mark an indifference to vulgar prejudice (conspicuous outrage).*

(4) *Sumptuous dress is not necessarily good. It must exhibit not only pecuniary strength, but the membership of a reputable class; for this reason it is uniform.*

(5) *The fashion of dress changes in accordance with changes in the productive forces of society. These manifest themselves in the following manners:*

(*a*) The growing pace and diffusion of fashion owing to the change in productive methods and increasing markets.

(*b*) *The catastrophic changes in fashion caused by the struggles and vicissitudes of the middle classes.*

(*c*) *The changes in the nature of the ruling class which was brought about by the industrial revolution, from which there resulted a new standard of sumptuosity and a new conception of vicarious consumption.*

(6) *Aesthetic appreciation of dress is to a great extent governed by the same laws as those which govern its development.*

It need scarcely be said that the view here summarised is not presented as the final and exact truth regarding this vast and complex department of social history. A true history can result only from the work of many scholars. All that is claimed is that here is the right entrance to the labyrinth; if others will but avail themselves of it, I am convinced that they will find their progress greatly advanced, and that many false turnings and blind alleys can be avoided thereby.

Still less does this brief adumbration of the theory of past fashions help us to prognosticate; it is tempting to speculate but it is exceedingly rash. Nor can one easily see an end to the process whereby imitation and mass production have accelerated emulation, so that now the change of years is accomplished in weeks, and it may soon be in days. Given modern productive methods a fashion might last no longer than a popular song. On the other hand the conditions of the market may change; the gap between the very rich and the middle classes may widen enormously with the concentration of capital in a few hands, and in that case the emulative process would again be weakened. There is also still a very large proportion of humanity whose interest in dress is, of bitter necessity, largely utilitarian.

Finally there is the possibility that the productive forces of the world may be released and made available to humanity at large, in such a manner that the full abundance of wealth now made possible by science may become universal. In such a state of affairs class distinctions would gradually be swamped from below and the pecuniary canons of taste would slowly lose their meaning; dress could than be designed to meet all the needs of the individual, and uniformity, which is essential to fashion, would disappear.

# APPENDICES

# APPENDIX A

## THE CLOTHING TRADE

THE process by which fashions arrive upon the market has been unduly simplified in Chapter Four in order that the main argument may be clearly stated; actually the relationship between producer and consumer is complicated by the fact that there is, as in almost any modern industry, a whole chain of producers buying from each other, of whom the *couturier* is but the last.

A correspondent with a first-hand knowledge of the distributive side of the industry writes:

I, for one . . . was progressively more firmly persuaded that no one "set the fashions" at all (in the late 'twenties), because they were predetermined, not even by the exclusive dressmakers, but by the purveyors of exclusive fabrics. A dressmaker worthy of the exclusive clientele she commanded, knew how to use the material better than you or I would. (Or I would.) Concretely: when the manufacturers had done a bit of experimental weaving of fine yarns or silks or whatever—which may itself have been determined by a natty new piece of machine tooling run up by some (British or American) machine tool manufacturer—they showed their new seasons patterns to the *couturiers*, and then it was up to them to find the right, the best, the acceptable way of arranging clothes made of that particular bit of stuff. Also, and this is quite inevitable under that particular system, it meant that at least half the "leaders of fashion" would be seen wearing that exact stuff in that precise shape; and as these people would never go anywhere unless they were quite certain all the others would be there too, it had more the character of a uniform than a very distinguished piece of personal good taste. Those are the things which struck me about the clothing racket when I saw it in close-up.

From which it will appear that there is no finding an end to the thread of connected interacting processes which go to the making of a fashion. No one individual has the last word.

It would appear that in a luxury trade the power of the consumer must be all important; on the other hand, where the consumer is actuated by snobbery he (or she) is very gullible.

The customer is always right, but there's a sucker born every minute.

## THE DRESS OF GHOSTS

THE dress of ghosts deserves more attention than it has received from students of costume, and much more erudition than I can bring to bear upon it. The following remarks are intended only to indicate the main lines upon which some student of psychical research might base a complete study.

The dead, it would appear, are exempt from all industrial labour; like the living in similar circumstances they mark this in their dress. There are, no doubt, many exceptions to this rule, but this would seem to be a pretty general trait of ghosts in Western Europe. Conspicuous Leisure is, however, marked in very different ways. In the first place there are the archaistic ghosts, who indeed rely for much of their effect upon the use of the clothes of their own times; these ghosts would appear to be indifferent to the influence of fashion; they appear, like Hamlet's father, "armed at point exactly, *cap-a-pe*"; it is, however, to be noticed that they do not push their love of anachronism to the point of being actually *démodé*; but allow a decent interval to elapse until their costume has become romantically distant and thus aesthetically acceptable. It will commonly be found that spirits of this kind belong to persons in the higher income groups, or are attached to respectable families in their places of residence.

If it were possible to photograph archaistic ghosts, their appearance would be of the greatest service to students of costume. Unluckily, they are shy of the camera. With the introduction of spirit photography a new style of ghostly attire comes into fashion. A cursory examination of spirit photographs suggests that this change, like other fashionable changes, has been gradual. At first (the earliest photographs date from the middle of the last century) the spirits, while declining to appear in archaistic dress, manifested themselves in shrouds and sheets, which were in an existing tradition; this dress has gradually been modified by the adoption of a new fabric called ectoplasm; the tendency has been to a greater and greater obliteration of the person in woolly clouds of this material.

Ghostly dress, as it appears in spirit photographs, would seem to show a pretty complete abandonment of conspicuous consumption; conspicuous outrage is also, happily, very uncommon, but conspicuous leisure remains a constant feature; ectoplasm no less than shrouds or sheets is an impediment to industrial activity. As we have seen, a noticeable feature of costume intended to exhibit a futile existence is unpractical footwear; in the case of ghosts the ideal of Chinese shoes is sometimes attained and surpassed by omitting the feet altogether.

It would seem, on a general view of supernatural modes, that the spirits of the departed are unmoved by personal vanity, and that their chief concern is to conform to the standards of those who survive.